DOWN THEY COME! UNITED STATES MARINES MAKING
THEIR GRADUATION LEAP

PARACHUTES

by HERBERT S. ZIM

ILLUSTRATED WITH DRAWINGS
BY JAMES MACDONALD
AND WITH PHOTOGRAPHS

HARCOURT, BRACE AND COMPANY
NEW YORK

COPYRIGHT, 1942, BY

HERBERT S. ZIM

I

PRINTED IN THE UNITED STATES OF AMERICA

*To the Amerian inventors and pilots
who developed the parachutes
and to our paratroopers
who use them so ably*

CONTENTS

ix

INTRODUCTION

AT the word "parachute" we think of a pilot leaping for his life from a disabled plane. But parachutes have other, though perhaps less important, uses than life saving. In tracing the story of the parachute, its development and its use, one must go far afield. In attempting this, I have had the help of many people who work directly or indirectly with parachutes.

For information and assistance I am deeply indebted to Lt. Col. D. P. Page, Bureau of Public Relations, War Department, and to the Public Relations Officers at Barksdale Field, Louisiana, Randolph Field, Texas, Maxwell Field, Alabama, Fort Benning, Georgia, and at the Army Air Forces, Washington, D. C. I have also to thank the Office of Public Relations, Secretary of the Navy, the Public Relations Officers at the U. S. Naval Air Station, Lakehurst, New Jersey, and at the Marine Barracks, Quantico, Virginia. Data

Introduction

from the U. S. Army Information Service, Second Corps Area, were most welcome.

Information on the civilian use of parachutes has come from the Civil Aeronautics Board, the Division of Air Mail Service, U. S. Post Office Department, and the Forest Service, U. S. Department of Agriculture. May I also thank Mr. Floyd Smith of the Pioneer Parachute Company, the Irving Air Chute Company, Mr. Harry R. Stringer of All American Aviation, and Mr. O. J. Mink of the Reliance Manufacturing Company, Parachute Division; finally the American-Russian Institute for the use of its library and files.

HERBERT S. ZIM

PARACHUTES

Chapter One

FROM AN IDEA TO REALITY

OVER two hundred years ago a parachute saved its first life, that of an imperiled balloonist. Even then the parachute was not a new invention. As man's venture into the air developed, the parachute played an increasingly important part. However, there were periods when parachutes were almost forgotten. Early aviators held them in disdain. Even the parachutist making the "leap for life" from a hot-air balloon failed to excite the carnival crowd. Men were slow in foreseeing the scope and future of the parachute.

From this unusual background emerged the modern parachute—less than twenty-five years ago. The first successful modern type chute was tried early in 1919. More recently, parachutes have been taken over as an instrument of war. Only five years ago we saw in the newsreels the first mass landing of troops by parachutes. In 1939 parachute troops had their initial test in battle.

Every year new uses for parachutes are being tried out. Doctors now drop by parachute at isolated farms or at airplane crashes. Trained parachutists drop near blazing forest fires and soon get them under control. Chutes bring food and supplies to a forest patrol. Nurses in Russia are dropped near the front lines by parachutes. Chutes are used by weather bureaus, exploring parties, aerial photographers, as well as by the army, navy, and marines.

Thousands of skilled, trained, valuable pilots have saved their lives with parachutes and with their aid have lived to fly again. Forts, cities, and airports have been attacked by parachute troops. Bloody battles have resulted—the air-borne invaders have often been victorious. Parachute ski troops can land and hold inaccessible peaks that would be difficult if not impos-

4

sible for ground troops to take.

The parachute is not a complicated machine. It is so simple that you will be surprised at the close resemblance of modern chutes to those built several hundred years ago. The word "parachute" explains itself. It comes from two French (and hence Latin) words literally meaning "to guard against falling." This is exactly what a parachute is designed to do. One of the earliest parachutes was designed to save a man trapped in a burning tower. Later parachutes were used with balloons and finally with airplanes.

It will always be exciting to use a parachute, and its use is increasing daily. There is nothing half-way about it. Jump—and your life depends on a few yards of silk, rope, and canvas. But if a parachute lets a pilot down—it lets him down safely. Parachutes are meant to work and they do. Just how they work, how they are used, and how they came to be is the subject of this story—the story of the parachute.

We can only speculate as to where man got his first ideas about parachutes. You may, if you wish, trace the parachute back to the gliding habits of birds and animals—hawks and flying squirrels, for example.

You might even want to consider the parachute seeds of dandelions, hawkweeds, and other common plants. We do have early written records in Chinese manuscripts that suggest these wise people had constructed a kind of parachute. The records are, unfortunately, vague. The Chinese made the umbrella. It is quite possible that the combination of an umbrella and a good stiff breeze might have suggested the idea of the parachute to an alert Chinese.

Late in the 15th century, that genius of all time, Leonardo da Vinci, entered into his notebooks opinions and ideas on the flight of birds. Da Vinci analyzed the mechanics of flight and drew conclusions that are still considered the basis of the science of aerodynamics. One of the sketches in his notebook shows a man descending by means of a crude parachute shaped roughly like a pyramid tent. The notes accompanying this diagram explain how the device is to be used.

While da Vinci made models of many of his numerous inventions, he did not actually make a working parachute. The idea was neglected for some time. A hundred years later, Veranzio, another Italian, de-

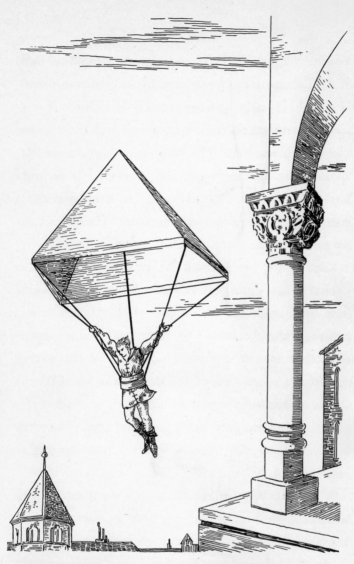

LEONARDO DA VINCI DESIGNED THIS PARA-
CHUTE WHICH WAS NEVER USED

scribed and pictured in a book on machines a parachute that seems to have been based on da Vinci's
model.

About the time of our own revolution in 1776,
France was experiencing a period of enlightenment,
of artistic and scientific advances. The Montgolfier
brothers were performing exciting experiments with
fires, hot air, and huge cloth bags. By 1783 their experiments succeeded in making the balloon an accom-
plished fact. At last man could leave the ground and
soar into the air. Even before they had perfected their
balloon, the Montgolfier brothers had made and tested
parachutes. There is one report of their climbing a
high tower and dropping a sheep safely to the ground
by means of a 7-foot parachute. But the records are
not clear as to what the Montgolfiers had in mind
with their parachute experiments. Some historians
think they merely experimented with parachutes as
part of their effort to make a balloon. Others believe
that a real honest-to-goodness parachute was their
aim.

At about the same time, Sebastien Lenormand, also
a Frenchman, jumped from a high tower using a

14-foot parachute. He apparently reached the ground uninjured and congratulated himself for having perfected a way of escaping safely from burning buildings. While Lenormand was satisfied to consider the parachute as a portable fire-escape, another Frenchman, J. P. Blanchard, was using the parachute in connection with the newly invented balloon. In 1785 Blanchard took a dog up with him in a balloon and dropped the animal safely to the ground with a chute. He performed many other parachute experiments, designing a silk parachute that could be folded up. All previous models were attached to a framework that held the cloth open. There is some doubt as to whether Blanchard actually jumped himself. It is reported that he did jump from a balloon in 1793, but broke his leg and gave up his experiments after that attempt.

Andrew Jacques Garnerin is given the credit of being the first parachutist. Garnerin made so many experiments and demonstrations that he undoubtedly deserves the credit, even if Blanchard actually made a jump before him.

October 22, 1797, was an exciting day in Paris.

GARNERIN WAS THE FIRST TO MAKE A SUC-
CESSFUL PARACHUTE JUMP

From an Idea to Reality

While crowds gaped, a large balloon filled with hot air from a roaring fire ascended. A balloon ascension was nothing new to the Parisians. For over ten years reckless men had soared over the chimney tops in gaily colored bags filled with hot air. This time a queer contraption hung under the basket of the balloon. It was a large parachute. When the hot air sent the balloon upwards, Garnerin hopped into the basket of his parachute and was carried along, dangling below the basket of the balloon. At the height of about 2,000 feet, the parachute was cut loose. It quickly opened and Garnerin descended, somewhat dazed but safe and triumphant.

Five years later, Garnerin, now a professional chutist, made a much more exciting jump before English royalty and notables. His new parachute was made of 32 silk panels sewn together into an inverted cup shape. It was 23 feet in diameter and was attached underneath the balloon basket. This time the balloon is believed to have risen about 8,000 feet before Garnerin cut loose. The parachute opened fully and Garnerin's fall was checked. But as this parachute fell through the air it began to oscillate. The basket at the end of the shroud lines swung from side to side in a dizzy arc, until it seemed as if Garnerin would be thrown out. The unfortunate parachutist reached the ground safely, but he was so shaken up and airsick from his ride that he scarcely noted the acclaim from the royal family when he got back to London.

Garnerin's jump became the topic of the day in London. People wrote to the papers offering suggestions and theories as to the cause of oscillation. Garnerin replied. A heated controversy on parachute theory arose and continued even after Garnerin returned to France. Garnerin kept up his experiments and demonstrations. He modified the design of his chute in an attempt to make it more steady.

Credit is given to the French astronomer Lelande, a contemporary of Garnerin's, for solving the problem of parachute oscillation. This scientist suggested that the air trapped in the canopy of the descending chute spilled out on one side, setting up a strain and causing uneven pressure on the edge of the canopy. This changing, uneven pressure rocked the canopy from side to side producing the swaying motion. He suggested that if the air were permitted to escape

OVER 150 YEARS AGO THE VENT HOLE AT THE APEX OF THE PARACHUTE FIRST REDUCED OSCILLATION. IT IS STILL USED IN MODERN CHUTES

through the top of the chute, the condition might be corrected. The parachute was tested with a round hole cut through at the apex of the dome. The idea worked. Oscillations were not completely eliminated but since then they have ceased to be an important problem.

Hot air balloons were dangerous affairs. The balloonist often burned bundles of straw under the bag to maintain his hot air supply. If the burning straw ignited the fabric, the balloon flight was brought to a sudden and dramatic halt. Such was the fate of a Polish balloonist, Kuparento, in the sky above Warsaw in July, 1808. But Kuparento had a parachute with him. As his flaming balloon plunged earthward, he grabbed his chute and jumped. The burning balloon tore past Kuparento as he hung in the air, supported by his parachute. The aerial life-saver did its work. When Kuparento tumbled over safely as his chute hit the ground, the first life had been saved.

A young English artist, Robert Cocking, who was in the large holiday crowd watching Garnerin, was much impressed by the jump. He was puzzled by the violent oscillations of the chute, that had nearly

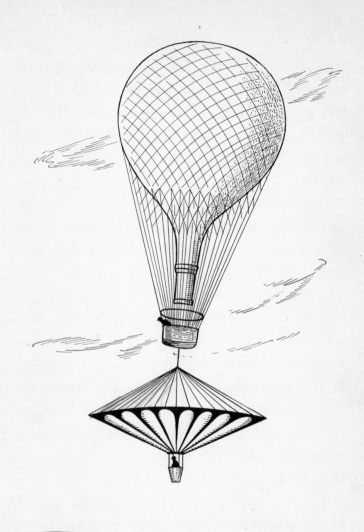

COCKING'S PARACHUTE UTILIZED A NEW
DESIGN BUT IT WAS NOT SUCCESSFUL

proved fatal to Garnerin. In the years that followed, Cocking worked on parachute designs and tested models that he hoped would eliminate the sway and make the parachute safer.

Some forty years later, in 1837, Cocking, now an old man, was ready to try out the model he had perfected. His parachute was very different from Garnerin's and wholly unlike any we use today. It was a huge cone-shaped affair, with the apex of the cone pointed downwards. The top of the parachute was attached to a 107-foot hoop. Other smaller hoops supported the lower sections. This contraption weighed over 200 pounds and used 124 yards of the finest available linen. On July 24, 1837, everything was ready and, despite the fears of his friends, Cocking decided to jump.

It was not until late in the afternoon that the balloon got into the air. Cocking had hoped to go up 8,000 feet, but at about 5,000 feet the balloonist could go no higher. Cocking released the catch holding the parachute to the balloon. The parachute started down rapidly in an uneven descent. The strain on it was too great. The upper rim broke. The cloth collapsed. About 300 feet from the ground the basket broke off and hurled the experimenter to his death.

Years later experiments showed that Cocking's idea was sound and that such a parachute would develop sufficient air resistance if properly constructed.

Cocking's failure did not discourage another Englishman, Hampton, from trying his parachute invention a year later. He descended safely from 6,000 feet in a 15-foot "umbrella" parachute.

Though Hampton made other jumps in the years that followed, parachuting was generally discouraged. A number of leading balloonists declared it impractical as a life preserver. In 1838, John Wise, an American balloonist, allowed his balloon to explode at 13,000 feet and reached earth safely, supported by the fragments of the bag. He repeated this feat the next year and expressed his belief that the damaged balloon was a better parachute than the parachute itself.

In the years that followed, parachuting found a place for itself. Not an important place—not even a respectable place. For the next fifty years parachutes were used only at circuses, carnivals, and exhibits.

17

Parachutes

Every circus had its captive balloon. For a small fee local townsfolk could have the thrill of rising up above the heads of their neighbors to look far out over the circus and the town. To attract customers, a parachute jump from a captive or free-sailing balloon might be arranged. The crowd would stare at the daring man slowly descending from the clouds. Later when the novelty wore off, parachutists had to rig a trapeze to their chutes and do tricks to amuse the customers while the chute slowly came to earth.

In this way parachuting became a skilled but unimportant trade, known only to a small group of daring men and women—for there were famous women jumpers too. These parachutists kept the tradition going. They readily responded when the call came to train the new generation of modern chutists.

Chapter Two

PARACHUTING GROWS UP

BY the early 19th century three uses for the parachute had been proposed. The first, to rescue people from burning towers, was never taken seriously. The second, to rescue aeronauts from falling balloons, was decried by the balloon experts of the period as unsafe and unnecessary. The third use, that of entertaining and thrilling crowds, was considered "vulgar." The parachute did not win early recognition. In fact, there were attempts to prohibit its use in England. Elsewhere for a period of about 100 years, parachuting was tied up closely with the use of balloons.

Parachutes

During the 19th century balloons were used in two ways. As captive balloons, anchored by a cable, they were used for military observation and to thrill circusgoers. These captive balloons were safe devices, even during wartime. In the Civil War observers in them directed gunfire. Stationed some distance behind the front lines, they were out of danger of enemy fire. Free flying balloons never passed the experimental and scientific stage. Altitude and cross country records were established. By dropping ballast, balloons could rise or hold their altitude. By releasing gas from the bag, the balloons could be brought slowly and safely to earth. In either case a parachute was unnecessary.

It was at this time that the parachute fell into disuse, except as a circus attraction. Nothing worth recording took place until 1885, when Captain Thomas Baldwin introduced a collapsible silk parachute. He used it in jumps from balloons. The end of the 19th century seemed a period of inactivity, but during this time the airplane was becoming a practical machine.

The airplane did not happen all at once. Years of work by many men preceded the Wright brothers' first successful flight in 1908. Once a successful flight was attained, aviation found itself. It grew by leaps and bounds, and parachuting grew up with it.

In the early experimental years of aviation few accurate records were kept. Because of this it is difficult to name the first man who used a parachute in connection with an airplane. Captain Albert Berry, an American, who had previously jumped from balloons, is sometimes given the credit for being first, but probably at least one other adventurer jumped from a plane before him. Late in 1911, Grant Morton is reported to have jumped from a Wright Model B plane, flying over Venice Beach, California. Morton carried his folded parachute in his arms. As he jumped he threw the canopy into the air. The parachute caught the wind and billowed open. Morton landed safely.

Captain Albert Berry, like his father John, was experienced with balloons and parachutes. Early in 1912 Thomas Benoist, who built planes and ran an aviation school near St. Louis, Missouri, announced a public exhibition of a parachute jump from an airplane. Albert Berry was to do the jumping. Twice the event was postponed because of unfavorable weather, but on March 1st Berry went up in a two-seater pusher plane. His 36-foot parachute was packed in a cone-shaped case underneath the fuselage. Instead of a harness it was equipped with a trapeze bar on which Berry sat. According to the plan he was to fly over the neighboring army barracks, descend, and deliver a message to the Commander. Over the parade grounds Berry climbed down to the axle of the plane, grasped the bar, and jumped from a height of 2,500 feet. The chute opened after two seconds. Berry landed shivering with cold but safe. He made another jump soon after to satisfy the customers who had been disappointed by previous inclement weather.

The chutes used by Morton and Berry were makeshift affairs. At that time no one in this country gave serious attention to designing parachutes scientifically. Just a year before, however, an Italian inventor named Pino received a patent for a flexible chute somewhat similar to those used today. The aviator using this new device wore his parachute in a pack like a knapsack. On his head was a hat that would be the envy of any woman. The leather cap blossomed out into a smaller open parachute. When the aviator jumped, the small pilot chute pulled off his hat and also hauled the large chute from the knapsack. The ideas embodied in Pino's parachute were sound. The pilot chute is still being used today.

Some early aviators expressed the opinion that parachutists jumping from a plane would upset its equilibrium and throw the plane out of control. Demonstrations proved their fears groundless. Even so, aviators still regarded parachuting as a circus trick. No aviator seriously considered parachutes as a safety device. They had reason for skepticism since many of the early makeshift parachutes failed to work properly. The man who jumped never had a chance if his chute failed to open properly. Furthermore, aviators in these early days often considered themselves dare-devils. Anybody who wore a parachute was either a sissy or a fool.

In French aviation circles a different spirit prevailed. Colonel Lalance offered a prize of 10,000 francs for a satisfactory parachute. This was in 1911. Over a dozen experimental parachutes were tried out from balloons and airplanes during the next two years. Some of these were complicated devices with springs to force the chute open. One was opened by a jet of compressed air. Others did not work at all. None solved the parachute problem, though the prize attracted inventors and stimulated research.

When the World War began in 1914 both the Allies and the Germans used captive balloons for observation purposes. But now the captive balloons were no longer safe. Enemy planes swooped down from the clouds and set them afire with tracer bullets. If the balloon could not be hauled down before it was hit, the observer met with certain death. Within a year the British and French equipped their balloons with parachutes packed in conical containers outside the basket. The Germans followed their example, using a chute developed by the woman parachutist, Kathe Palus, a celebrated exhibition jumper. The Americans adopted the French balloon parachute when we entered the war. It is reported that the lives of over 800 balloonists were saved by parachute jumps.

The airplanes used for scouting and attack during World War I were weak contraptions of wood, cloth, and wire. Their pilots called them "crates," a name they well deserved. They were delicate and insecure, capable of losing a wing or a tail at the slightest shakeup. Their vital parts had no protection. The engine, gas tank, and pilot were all exposed. A hit from a single machine gun bullet might prove fatal and often did. Without a parachute the loss of a plane meant the loss of a pilot, too. Pilots rarely escaped alive from a crackup. Figures actually showed a pilot on active duty at the front could not expect to live more than two months. Thousands of aviators lost their lives. Many had to leap from burning planes, and would have lived if they had only had a chute.

By 1917 airplane parachutes were desperately needed. The British took over the "Guardian Angel" parachute that had been developed by E. R. Calthorp. This parachute was one of the so-called "automatic" types. A cord connected the pilot's harness with the chute. When the pilot leaped from a disabled plane, the tightening cord pulled the parachute from its container. Occasionally the cord fouled and broke. To prevent accidents that resulted from having the chute separated from the pilot, the Guardian Angel was modified to be worn by the pilot in a pack. A canvas strip extended from the chute to the floor of the plane. As the pilot jumped this strip unwound, finally pulling the chute from the pack.

Further improvements were made on the Guardian Angel the following year. At the same time the Germans experimented with two types of parachutes. A small pilot chute was used to pull the large parachute from the pack. The parachute was worn in a seat pack and used with a static line, similar to the Guardian Angel.

While these experiments were going on, the war came to an end. The pilots returned home, the "crates" were left to rust, and the parachutes stored away and forgotten.

Back in the United States, experiments with parachutes were making progress at McCook Field. Instead of dropping this work at the end of the war, the U. S. Army continued its efforts to develop the best practical parachute for American aviators. The work at McCook Field, Dayton, Ohio, started in the summer of 1918. The army allotted funds for a complete study of parachutes, and was fortunate in securing the services of Floyd Smith, a leading expert. When the armistice was signed all war efforts ceased. But in the excitement of demobilization no one ordered Floyd Smith to terminate his work. Smith was too interested to want to stop anyhow. He went right ahead with his experiments. The following year the War Department, realizing the importance of this project, put Major E. L. Hoffman in charge of the work. The Major rallied a staff of active, enthusiastic men around him. From then on America took the lead in parachute research and construction. The early experiments at McCook Field led to major changes in parachute design.

Chapter Three

THE PARACHUTE COMES OF AGE

THE parachute unit at McCook Field set to work in earnest. Invitations to submit parachute designs were sent to scientists, inventors, and aviation experts. Plans and blue-prints began to arrive in Dayton with every mail. Inventors and government representatives came, bringing with them models for testing. All of these parachutes were tested with a dummy, the size and weight of an average man. The materials were carefully analyzed. The weak points and the strong points of each model were determined and recorded.

Parachutes tested at McCook Field were automatic

chutes of two general types: in one type, the parachute and its container were attached to the plane. The pilot wore a harness with a rope connecting to the parachute. The second type was worn by the aviator, but a cord connected the chute to the plane. In either case the aviator had only to jump. When he reached the end of his rope, the parachute was automatically pulled from its container.

Major E. L. Hoffman and his staff were disappointed in the results of hundreds of tests made during their first year. None of the models met their strict requirements. Floyd Smith and others suggested that the group study a free type of parachute. This would be attached only to the aviator. There were to be no connections to the plane at all—no ropes to foul or break. This free type of chute would be released from the pack by the operator *after* he had jumped.

Many an expert expressed the firm conviction that a hand-operated chute would never work. Some pointed out that the aviator would lose consciousness as soon as he leaped from the plane. Others believed he would remain conscious but would fall so fast that he could not control his actions. The jumper might be paralyzed by fear and would not pull the rip cord in time. All of these objections were duly considered. Yet the parachute staff realized that without a test no one could be sure. The free type of parachute had been tested over and over again with the dummy. A rope attached to the rip cord simulated the pull that a falling chutist would give. The chute worked every time. The first model, known as Model A, was a 28-foot parachute made of straight cut silk. The canopy was composed of 40 panels with 40 braided shroud lines. It had a 40-inch vent hole at the apex of the canopy controlled by thick rubber bands and was packed in a back-type pack. This model was later altered to a 24-foot size in a seat pack. In both packs the dummy tests proved all that could be expected.

Floyd Smith and Leslie L. Irvin had worked on the new free-type parachute. Both these men had long records as exhibit jumpers. Because of their experience they challenged the experts who claimed that a man lost consciousness as he fell through the air. These two belonged to the small selected group that

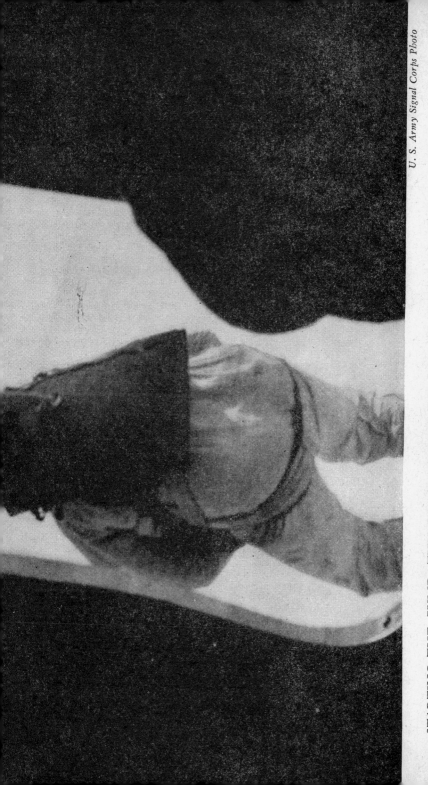

STARTING THE JUMP. THIS PARACHUTE IS OPENED BY A CORD OR STATIC LINE ATTACHED

TO THE PLANE

knew parachutes. They had used them at carnivals and circuses. They had made their living with parachutes and had entrusted their lives to the silk canopy many times.

Leslie Irvin was the younger of the pair. He had been interested in flying and in parachutes as long as he could remember. Way back before he had reached his teens, he and some other boys made a hot air balloon. They sent a cat up as a passenger and chased the balloon till a strong breeze carried the unwilling cat out over the Pacific. When a local inventor decided to build a plane, Irvin, then fourteen, hung around and aided in the work. Soon after, on the basis of this experience he got a job helping Barney Oldfield, the famous stunt driver. Oldfield, in his auto, raced a plane around an exhibit track. Irvin acted as ballast in the racing car and helped care for both machines. Later he worked on a small dirigible, flying over Los Angeles with a load of paying passengers. When this enterprise failed, Irvin did balloon work for Universal Pictures. Experience piled up fast, though Irvin was still a young man. At the age when most young people first begin to think about a job he had already worked for years with planes, balloons, and chutes.

Irvin drifted to carnivals doing all kinds of work. He did a high dive from a 70-foot tower. Then he went into parachuting and did stunt jumps. "Ski-Hi Irvin" began to be featured on carnival billboards all over the country. But while busy with his work, Irvin still had time to plan parachutes and think about parachute problems. "Why should a parachutist lose consciousness?" wondered Irvin, recalling his high dives. He had been fully conscious from the instant he left the platform till he landed. He could remember everything he saw and felt as he dove through the air. Irvin had ideas such as these in mind when he heard of the parachute experiments at McCook Field. He promptly offered his services to Major Hoffman and was put to work making the first free-falling chute.

Floyd Smith was another man with air in his blood. For years, too, he had worked at carnivals and circuses as an acrobat and aerialist. In 1912 he gave up circus work, built his own plane, and taught himself to fly. With this homemade crate Smith went barnstorming all over the West and down into Mexico. He had all sorts of trouble and narrow escapes, but from them Smith learned about planes and flying.

In 1914 Smith was test pilot for Glenn Martin, who had begun to build planes at Los Angeles. Here, too, Smith had more narrow escapes. Once a plane lost a wing and only his skill in maneuvering the disabled ship saved Smith's life when he landed. It is not surprising that Smith became interested in parachutes. He had ideas and spoke to the men at the Glenn Martin plant about them.

When this country entered World War I, Floyd Smith did his part as chief inspector of aircraft production. While he was busy at this work, the commander of the American Air Forces in France faced a serious problem. The job of a pilot was at that time the most dangerous in the army. The loss of a plane invariably meant the loss of the pilot. A good pilot was valuable and hard to get, so it was no wonder that the high loss of life worried the officers at headquarters.

It was just at this critical time that a staff officer recalled Floyd Smith and his ideas about parachutes.

THIS PILOT WEARS A HAND-OPERATED CHUTE. HE IS
REACHING FOR THE RIP CORD THAT HE WILL PULL WHEN
HE IS CLEAR OF THE PLANE

The word went to headquarters and a cable flashed
across the ocean shifting Smith from inspecting work
to parachute experiments. Just as Smith got started,
the armistice was signed. Smith continued nevertheless and the year following the army took up the parachute problem in earnest. Smith continued to work

on the hand-operated chute.

The time was ripe to subject the free-falling chute to the crucial test. Irvin volunteered for the job. The day was set for April 28, 1919, and the entire Parachute Unit turned out to watch. Floyd Smith piloted the plane, which rose in a slow spiral and circled over the field. The plane leveled off at 1,500 feet. Smith gave the signal. Irvin climbed from his seat and jumped. On the ground the tense group saw the figure climb out of the cockpit. They saw it leap clear of the plane. A white streamer floated out behind the parachutist. The wind caught the canopy and it billowed open. In a short time Irvin was on the ground. He broke an ankle in landing, but this was no fault of the chute.

The first real test with a free-falling chute was a success. Soon after, Floyd Smith repeated the jump as did Ralph Bottreil of the army staff. Others followed and the new type parachute was accepted.

Tests of other chutes still continued. In July, 1919, Lieutenant Caldwell of the British Air Corps came to McCook Field to demonstrate the latest Guardian Angel chute. This was the best automatic type chute used in the First World War. The officer went up to give his exhibition as the members of the Parachute Unit watched on the field below. Lieutenant Caldwell jumped. His life line pulled tight, but as the parachute pulled from its container it caught on the plane. The line broke and the Lieutenant fell to his death.

The death of Caldwell finally condemned the automatic chute. The experts at McCook Field were more than ever convinced that their free-falling chute was the perfect aerial life preserver. They persuaded pilots to wear chutes when going aloft. The attitude of airmen changed. They began to have confidence in the bundle harnessed to them. After an unfortunate accident—the death of an officer who crashed after leaving the parachute behind on the ground—the wearing of a parachute became compulsory. An order directing that every person going aloft in an army plane must wear an approved chute was posted at all flying fields. Still, as every aviator knew, the parachute had not yet saved the life of a single person in an airplane. Three years passed before the first life was saved.

At McCook Field Major Hoffman and his men almost hoped for an accident so that their chute would get a chance to prove its worth. On October 20, 1922, Lieutenant Harold R. Harris took up a Loening monoplane to test further a new type of balanced ailerons. These ailerons had been tested at low speeds and Harris was ordered to give them a real trial. Harris went up and, meeting another plane from the field, went into fighting practice high above Dayton. The planes dove at each other, banked and zoomed up again.

Coming out of a shallow turn at 150 miles an hour, the stick of the Loening monoplane suddenly started a rapid vibration. Harris grabbed tight but could not hold it still. The whole plane shook violently and headed into a 30-degree dive. Parts of the wing tore off and were blown away. There was only one thing for Harris to do. He had never used a chute before—never had any practice—but he climbed out of the cockpit and the wind carried him over the side.

Harris reached for the rip cord and pulled. Nothing happened. He pulled again but he still continued to fall. A third time he yanked hard, and, as he tumbled over in the air, he realized that he was not pulling the rip cord at all, but at the harness ring on his thigh. Falling upside down he had grasped the wrong ring. He carefully reached for the correct ring only a few inches away. A sharp pull—and a second later a loud snap. The chute was open. Below, Harris could see a school building and some houses. Seconds later he landed on the grape arbor of a neighbor. The police came and an ambulance, but except for the bruises he had received from the vibrating stick, Harris was unhurt. The monoplane crashed and burned nearby.

Thus the parachute passed its final test. Harris fell about 2,000 feet while he was trying to pull his harness ring. His chute opened about 500 feet from the ground and worked perfectly once it had opened. The first emergency jump from a heavier than air machine was a complete success. You could depend on the parachute.

Chapter Four

CLOSE-UP OF A PARACHUTE

MEMBERS of a fighter or bomber command wear different clothes depending on the climate and on the altitude they expect to fly. Each and every crew member, no matter what his designation, is rigged up in a series of wide straps that seem to be attached to a seat cushion. If you knew nothing about planes or pilots, it might strike you as odd that every man carries his own cushion. Of course, this affair of straps and cushion is a parachute. It is specially designed so the aviator sits on it while flying and actually uses it as a cushion. In addition, a pad of sponge rubber between his body and the parachute pack makes the cushion quite comfortable.

It is the rule of all military services—army, navy and marines—that every member of the plane's crew wear a parachute when aloft. Even some civilian and commercial planes have chutes attached to each seat so they can be connected in a jiffy. The strict rule about parachutes is a good one. It is impossible to keep records up-to-date in these times, but certainly the number of men whose lives were saved with the aid of these clumsy seat cushions runs into thousands.

The parachute used by military aviators and those approved by the Civil Aeronautics Board are made according to exact specifications. Each material used in the chutes and pack must pass rigid government tests. So must the completed parachute before it is put into service.

A parachute ready for use consists of five major parts. Most important is the canopy—the huge white cup-shaped bag. Long cords called shroud lines or suspension lines connect the canopy to the harness. The harness is a series of straps that support the para-chutist when he is in the air. Attached to this harness is a canvas pack into which the entire parachute is carefully folded. The rip cord is part of the pack. When it is pulled, the flaps of the pack are released. The fifth part of the parachute, the part most people do not see, is a small pilot chute that opens as soon as the rip cord is pulled and helps draw the main chute from the pack.

These five parts of the chute—canopy, shroud lines, pilot chute, harness, and pack—must each do their part if the parachute is to work properly. These parts form a chain on which the life of the airman depends. A weakness in any link is likely to be fatal. A ripped canopy may be just as dangerous as fouled shroud lines. In making the parachute, the strength of each of these parts is carefully determined. Any strain on the canopy must also be sustained by the shroud lines and harness. Each part is tested to stand strains much greater than those usually expected when the chute is operated.

The canopy is usually made of a specially selected, untreated silk known as Habuti. More recently pongee silk has been used and silk substitutes. Cotton, nylon, and other substitutes for silk are bulkier and heavier.

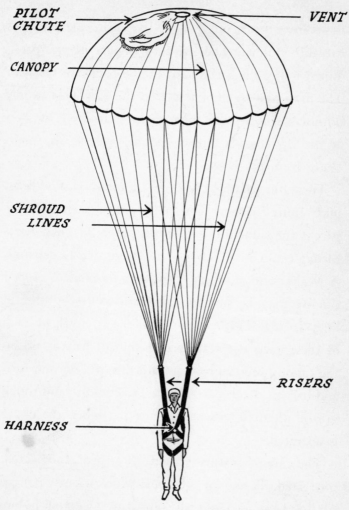

PILOT CHUTE

VENT

CANOPY

SHROUD LINES

RISERS

HARNESS

HERE ARE ALL THE PARTS OF A PARACHUTE
EXCEPT THE PACK, HIDDEN BEHIND THE
JUMPER

They do not stand up as well under severe strain, but for ordinary use they are serviceable and dependable.

Most silks used in clothing and decoration are treated with chemicals to make them heavier and improve their sheen. But these chemicals weaken the silk. Only natural, untreated silk is used in parachutes. The silk must be strong. It must not pull apart (tensile strength) under a strain of 40 pounds per square inch. It must not burst under a strain of 140 pounds per square inch. Despite its strength, parachute silk is very light. One square yard weighs between 1.3 and 1.6 ounces. About 70 yards of this silk are used in making the standard 28-foot parachute. When treated with care parachute silk is very durable. A chute may be safely used for a period of eight to ten years. However, if oil or chemicals get into the silk, its life is shortened.

In making the canopy the silk is cut at an angle or bias. Cutting in this way distributes the strain more evenly and limits the possibility of a rip or tear. The canopy is made of pieces of silk of four different sizes. Twenty-four pieces of each size are cut, making a

96 PIECES OF SILK MADE THE 24 PANELS IN THE PARA-
CHUTE'S CANOPY

total of 96 parts to the canopy. Four pieces of silk (one of each size) are sewn together into a long triangular section or gore. Twenty-four of these triangular panels make up the canopy of the chute.

Putting the parts of the canopy together is an exacting job. The silk is sewn with a special machine. Each seam is reinforced with four rows of stitching. A special sewing machine folds and pulls the cloth as it is sewn, so the pieces fit exactly. Someone has estimated that there are over a quarter of a million stitches in the canopy. Each one of these must be perfect. Even the thread used is of the best silk, and must meet government specifications for parachute use.

The twenty-four panels are sewn together with the point of each triangle at the apex of the chute. These sections do not completely meet. An 18-inch hole is formed at the top of the chute. This vent hole permits an escape of air to hold the chute steady in its descent. As each panel is sewn into place, it is also bound with 1-inch silk tape that has been tested to withstand a 300-pound pull. At this stage the shroud lines are also sewn into place, each line fitting along the seam between the panels of the chute.

The shroud lines are made of braided silk, three-ply, each of thirty-two threads. Each shroud line is tested for a breaking strength of 400 pounds. Each is carefully stretched under pressure, measured and marked before it is sewn into place. In this way, every line bears exactly the same share of strain when the chute opens. If one line were a bit shorter there would be more strain on it than on the others. There are twelve shroud lines, each 60 feet long. These are stretched completely across the canopy with about 16 feet of loose line at each end. The suspension lines cross at the apex of the canopy and continue down the other side. This produces twenty-four ends and is much stronger than if twenty-four cords had been used instead of twelve. The suspension lines are sewn into place along the panel seams and are reinforced with tape. The twenty-four cords are grouped into bundles of six. Each group is attached to one of the four D rings on the harness.

The pilot chute is attached to the main chute at the point where the suspension lines cross the vent hole. The pilot chute is also made of silk and is about one yard in diameter. The small shroud lines that connect it to the main chute can withstand a strain of 100 pounds. The canopy of the pilot chute is supported by steel ribs. These are attached to a spring in such a way that the pilot chute is forced open as soon as the flaps of the pack are released. At first it was thought that the pilot chute was essential in pulling the main chute open. Experiments showed that the main chute will open pretty rapidly by itself. However, the pilot chute catches the wind of the propeller and carries the main chute straight out behind the plane. This lessens the danger of the suspension lines fouling the plane's tail. Once the canopy of the main chute has opened, the pilot chute collapses, as there is no current of air to support it.

The greatest strain on a parachute occurs at the moment it opens. It is equivalent to putting the brakes on a car speeding over 100 miles an hour. The shock of being stopped suddenly, when falling at a great speed, would be very serious for the parachutist if he didn't have a well-made harness to protect him. The harness is so arranged as to support the jumper's body at four points: both shoulders and

U. S. Army Signal Corps Photo

' THE WIND IS STRONG, THE JUMPER CANNOT ALWAYS
STEER HIS CHUTE SUCCESSFULLY

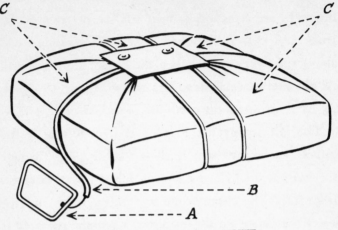

PARTS OF A PACKED CHUTE
A RIP CORD
B RIP CORD HOUSING
C FLAPS OF PACK

both thighs. In this way shock and pressure are distributed. After the first jar of the opening chute the jumper rides down safely and in comfort. The harness is adjustable to fit the wearer. Each pilot keeps his own chute properly adjusted.

The harness is made of linen webbing tested to a breaking strength of 3,000 pounds. The exact arrangement differs with the way the parachute is packed, but in all cases the harness gives the same kind of support to the aviator's body. The supporting webs are attached to four lift straps: two in the front and two at the back. These lift straps extend above the flyer's head, when the parachute is opened. At the end of each strap is a metal D ring to which six of the suspension cords are attached.

The last important part of the parachute is the canvas pack, into which all the other parts, except the harness, fit. The pack is attached to the harness. It protects the chute while it is being worn and releases the chute almost instantly when the rip cord is pulled. The canvas pack is supported by a wire frame. It has four large flaps which fold over and cover the chute. It has a series of pockets into which the shroud lines are carefully tucked. Either the parachutist or a licensed rigger packs the chute in a very definite way. The flaps are folded into place and are held shut by two metal pins that fit through the locking cone. These metal pins are attached to a thin, strong wire cable, ending in a metal ring. The wire cable is housed in a flexible metal tube that prevents it from catching on any part of the pack. All of these together make up the rip cord assembly. Pulling the ring draws out the pins holding the flaps in place. Once the rip

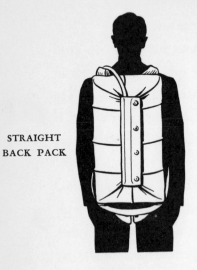

STRAIGHT
BACK PACK

SEAT PACK

FRONT
SUSPENSION
PACK

BACK PACK
AND
RESERVE
CHUTE
(FOR
TRAINING

TYPES OF PARACHUTE PACKS

cord is pulled, the chute opens automatically.

Seat and back pack parachutes have the rip cord located on the left thigh, so the jumper reaches across his body with his right hand to pull the cord. On front pack chutes the rip cord is at the right side. It does not have the long metal housing needed for the other types of chutes.

When the rip cord is pulled, the two pins are pulled from their socket. Heavy elastic cords pull the flaps back. The pilot chute whips out and in less than two seconds, the entire chute is open. Chutes made by different companies differ slightly in detail and in the way they are packed. But they must all meet government specifications before they can be sold.

Most parachutes used in military planes are packed in a seat pack. The flyers sit on them and are thus freed from any weight or bulk when in flight. However, the seat pack is not the best for every situation, and some parachutes are packed in other ways, depending on the conditions within the plane. A front suspension pack is used by machine gunners and photographers. Here the chute hangs on the aviator's stomach. This might seem clumsy, but is actually

IN TRAINING, TWO CHUTES ARE USED—A 28-FOOT STAND-
ARD CHUTE AND A 24-FOOT EMERGENCY CHUTE. A RIPPED
PANEL FORCED THIS JUMPER TO OPEN HIS EMERGENCY
CHUTE

more convenient and comfortable for the men who
run a camera or machine gun. The straight back pack
fits close to the back of the aviator and is convenient
for a person who may have to climb out on the rig-

ging of a plane or who has to move around. This type of pack is used in training. For small planes there is another arrangement. The pilot wears only the harness. The pack with the parachute is attached close at hand. In an emergency the harness is quickly connected to the pack with two strong clips and the parachute is ready for use.

The last type of pack is one designed to fit on the chairs of passenger planes. Passengers can attach them quickly, if they are needed, by slipping into the harness and fastening a few catches.

The standard 28-foot parachute is packed in all these different ways, so it can be convenient and comfortable in all airplane situations. Each of these packs weighs about the same: 21 pounds for the entire outfit. The canopy and shroud lines alone weigh about 18 pounds.

Chapter Five

TEST AND RETEST

O NCE a parachute is finished, inspected, tested and tucked away in its pack, it may be hauled around by pilot after pilot for five or six years or more before it may finally be condemned and discarded. There is little chance that it will ever be used in an emergency—if it is used at all. But if the day comes when a pilot must jump, the parachute must not fail. To keep the parachute in perfect condition during its entire life is no easy task. It is a task that cannot be bungled.

Even before it is built, the job of keeping the parachute fit is under way. The army and navy have strict specifications covering every bit of material that enters into the making of the chute. They issue directions regarding the workmanship on every essential part. Manufacturers are practically required to meet the army and navy specifications. After all, even in peace times these two are the biggest customers. Government specifications have set the pace and no manufacturer would think of investing his money in chutes that could not meet these tests. He would have no chance against competitors if he did.

Even if chutes are made to meet the specifications for webbing, silk, sewing thread, and D rings, there is still much to be done. The manufacturer's inspectors must check every seam and the workmanship thoroughly. Then a model, for which government approval is desired, is submitted to the proper authorities. The army, navy, and Civil Aeronautics Board each conduct tests for parachutes. The Aeronautics Board will accept data from army or navy tests.

Let's go along with a manufacturer who desires to obtain a certificate for a new model chute. Let us follow him to the Civil Aeronautics Board where his task may be simpler. The chute must be made of materials at least as good as those specified by the army or navy. Our manufacturer will have to submit technical data, test records, and information showing the breaking strength, weight, thread count, tensile strength, and data on all other chute characteristics on which there are specifications. This is just the beginning.

He must show that all parts of the harness can take a shock load greater than the combined strength of the shroud lines to which they are attached. All metal parts must stand their designed load without yielding. The material in the canopy must not contain gum or any filler. It must be free from blemishes that affect its strength or durability. The suspension lines must be continuous and should have no knots or splices. Before these lines are sewed into place each must be stretched under a 40-pound load and marked at the point of attachment. The sewing must be done in certain specific ways and the rip cord must withstand a pull of 300 pounds. The jumper must be able to release himself from the harness while in the air— so he may drop free if he is over water. Each chute pack must have a pocket containing a record card and packing instructions.

The manufacturer certifies to all these points and supports his contention with technical drawings and tables. With these records must go a description of the manufacturing practices in assembling the chute. If the administrator approves the chute on the basis of these data, the manufacturer returns home. He then arranges to have a plane and pilot ready and makes an appointment for the inspector to come and continue the tests.

Now the chute is ready for its functional tests. It is packed on a 170-pound dummy and taken up in a plane. The plane must cruise over the field at 70 miles per hour, at altitudes of not more than 500 feet. The dummy is dropped. The inspector keeps an eye on his stop watch. If the chute does not open within three seconds, it cannot be certified. When it reaches the ground the chute is repacked and the test is done over again. This test is repeated again and again and again—a total of twelve drops in all. No chance of an inferior chute getting through by luck.

After the twelfth drop, the chute is again repacked, but this time the suspension lines are purposely

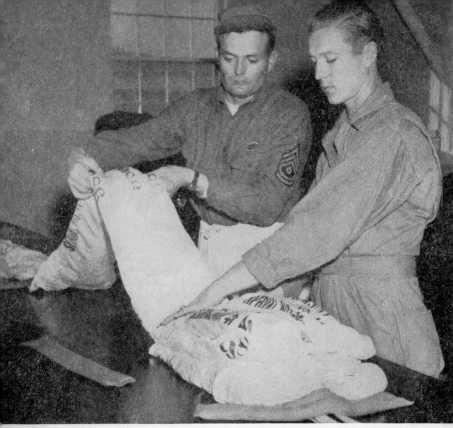

PACKING A CHUTE MUST BE DONE EXACTLY RIGHT. HERE
ARE TWO EXPERT RIGGERS PACKING AN ARMY PARACHUTE

twisted three times near the skirt of the canopy. In
this condition the chute is dropped again. It must
fully open within four seconds. This test is repeated
five times. Certainly this would seem enough—but
not for the Board. Now the harness is loaded with a

60

600-pound lead weight and the plane is speeded up to 100 miles per hour. The chute is dumped at 500 feet. When it lands it is closely examined for any tears or weaknesses. If none appears the test is repeated three times.

The chute has nearly proven its worth. It is now given two live drops. A man weighing about 170 pounds jumps from 2,000 feet. He must report no undue shock as the chute opens and must be able to step out of the harness without difficulty when he lands. Then the man jumps again from 2,500 feet while the inspector clocks his fall accurately. The rate of fall must not be greater than 21 feet per second.

If the parachute comes through 100% on all these tests, a certificate will be issued and the manufacturer can make and sell the chute, but he cannot alter the design or materials used in it without further testing and approval.

Only after rigid testing are chutes put in service. Once they are in use, this same rigid testing program continues. Even if the chute is not used, it must be opened, inspected, tested, and repacked every sixty

PARACHUTES DRYING AT RANDOLPH FIELD, TEXAS. EVERY
60 DAYS CHUTES MUST BE OPENED, AIRED, INSPECTED,
AND REPACKED

days. The man who does this work has a special license. When he signs the record card certifying his work, the job must be perfect. At these inspections minor repairs may be made. If the chute is at all moist, it is thoroughly dried and carefully checked. Moisture is an enemy of silk and a musty chute may deteriorate rapidly.

Every two years during the first four years of its use, the chute is scheduled to be drop-tested. After that it is drop-tested yearly for two or three years before it is retired from army life. The chute is taken up in a plane and dropped from 500 feet with a 170-pound dummy. The dummy is made in human form but without arms or legs. It is of canvas and leather properly weighted and balanced.

These dummies are very popular at air fields and parachute plants, where they do their regular work. "Dummy Sam" was the original. He worked at Mc-Cook Field testing all the experimental models. "Buck Private Dummy" of Randolph Field and "Elmer" of the Reliance Manufacturing Company have both led a rough life. The Irving Air Chute Company honors

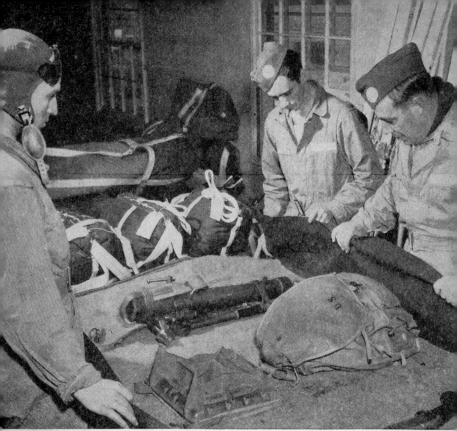

PACKING A SMALL MORTAR AND EQUIPMENT FOR PARA-
CHUTE DELIVERY

their dummy with a picture of it in their chute service manual.

The army dummies are dropped from the bomb
racks of huge bombers. Sometimes they are pushed
out of cabin doors. Invariably they are eased to the

Southeast Air Corps Training Center Photo

EVERY 2 YEARS CHUTES ARE DROP-TESTED WITH MAN-SIZED DUMMIES. THE BOMBER HAS JUST DROPPED THE DUMMIES AND THE PILOT CHUTES ARE PULLING THE BIG CANOPIES OPEN

ground under an open canopy and hauled away for another trip. The drop-tested chute is observed while it falls and after it has landed. If it has opened promptly and worked perfectly it is inspected and repacked.

With all these tests there is very little or no chance of a chute going wrong. There is some wear and tear as the chute gets older. After three years of army use the harness may be replaced. In three more years the chute has lived its lifetime if it has been doing military work. A civilian chute does not lead so hard a life and may be used a bit longer, if it is in good condition.

There is one last kind of testing that you will probably hear more about in years to come. It is research testing of parachutes. Strange as it may seem, no one knows very much about chutes. There are many questions about them that experts cannot answer. One reason for this is the fact that it is difficult to test and measure parachutes. A wind tunnel cannot be used. Observation of chutes during jumps can only be done in a limited way.

Floyd Smith, who was so active in the early days

Courtesy of Floyd Smith, Pioneer Chute Company

THIS TOWER IS THE LAST WORD IN PARACHUTE TESTING. THE CHUTES ARE SWUNG AT SPEEDS UP TO 300 MILES PER HOUR. A MOVIE CAMERA RECORDS DETAILS AS THE CHUTE OPENS

of parachuting, continues to be active today. He and his son perfected a parachute testing apparatus in 1940. The testing tower was erected near their parachute factory at Manchester, Connecticut. This is a 50-foot steel tower with a swinging boom. Powered by a 320 H.P. motor, it can swing a parachute around at the end of a cable at speeds of 70 to 350 miles per hour. A dummy fitted with a parachute is attached to the boom cables. The motor is started and, when the apparatus is swinging at the desired speed, the parachute is released by a cable control. The same cable sets in operation a motion picture camera attached to the boom, pointing at the dummy. This camera is speeded up 7.5 times. It follows the whirling chute and records every movement as the parachute opens. When the film is developed the engineers have a slow-motion analysis of a chute opening under known conditions.

Such an engineering device makes it possible to investigate many of the problems of parachute operation. One of the first things revealed on the motion picture film was that the pilot chute did not always pull the main canopy out from the pack as it was intended. Since chutes of some designs operate without a pilot chute, it was possible to investigate this problem scientifically. Chutes that turn inside out, that foul suspension lines or canopies, can be studied here, safely and scientifically.

No one appreciates the value of this instrument

more than the designer of the Russell Lobe Chute. When Mr. Russell, a parachute engineer, was perfecting his chute at San Diego a number of years ago, he attempted to solve some of these very problems. Men working with Russell risked their lives over and over again jumping from planes in every conceivable position in an attempt to discover what caused suspension lines to "line over" or pull across over the canopy. Now this can be done without risk.

The story of testing is not especially dramatic or heroic. Drop tests, inspections, and packing get to be routine jobs, but it is due to this constant vigilance that no aviator hesitates, in an emergency, to place his life into the hands of the men who designed, made, and packed his parachute.

Chapter Six

FALLING BODIES

IN one respect people and flounders are somewhat alike. Both live on the bottom. Flounders
live on the bottom of the sea and we live on
the bottom of an ocean of air. It is impossible to study
the flounder—how it lives and swims—without paying a good deal of attention to the sea on whose bottom it lives. The same applies to people using parachutes. The parachute is merely used to get a person
safely and easily back to the bottom of his ocean of
air. The nature of the air is just as important to a
parachutist as the ocean is to a flounder.

The ocean of air extends above the earth to heights

Falling Bodies

Not so long ago it would have been easy to avoid discussing this question at all. Airplanes didn't venture to heights above 15,000 or 18,000 feet. Below that level, as far as people and parachutes go, the air is fairly uniform. The variations do not make a great deal of difference. But now planes go up 30,000 and 35,000 feet, up to the sub-stratosphere where the air is thin and cold. This is the reason why we must consider the matter of altitude.

The air is all around us. Neither the person on the ground, nor the pilot, nor the parachutist in the air can escape its influence. Yet if we want to understand completely how a parachute works, what happens to a man jumping from a fast-moving plane, we must first set aside all thoughts about the air and consider the world as if the air didn't exist.

We must realize right from the start that talking as though the air does not exist does not change the facts. Before we are through we shall return to the existing ocean of air and see how it really affects parachutes and falling objects.

For a long time scientists have been concerned with the way things fall. The early Greeks debated the sub-

ject. But it was not until 1590, when Galileo performed his remarkable experiments, that the question
of falling objects was cleared up. Galileo climbed the
famous Leaning Tower at Pisa in Italy and carefully
timed heavy and light balls he dropped from the top
balcony. Then he spent days rolling balls of different
materials down slanting boards. As a result of his experiments Galileo reached some remarkable conclusions that still remain true today.

Nearly a hundred years later Sir Isaac Newton
carefully repeated Galileo's experiments and did
others of his own. From the facts he gathered, Newton was able to state even more clearly what happens
to objects when they fall through the air.

Now let us get to the facts as discovered by Galileo
and Newton. Remember we are talking as though air
didn't exist. Under such conditions all objects will
fall at exactly the same speed. A feather, a baseball, or
a five-ton boulder pushed off a cliff at the same time
would reach bottom at exactly the same second. They
would be pulled down by the gravitational pull of the
earth—a pull that varies with the distance from the
center of the earth, but not with the weight of the

object. Careful measurements of falling objects or objects that are partly falling, such as those rolling down a smooth board, show that they all fall at the same speed and that this speed increases at a uniform rate. This increase in speed, or acceleration, is always an increase of 32 feet per second per second.

Thirty-two feet per second per second is not a printer's mistake. It is the way in which an *increase* in speed is written. Speed itself is the distance traveled in a given time, such as 100 miles per hour, 32 feet per second. However, increase in speed means a change. When a man steps on the accelerator of his car, he is increasing and changing the speed. A person may be driving his car at a definite speed, say 30 miles an hour, 44 feet per second. He wants to pass a car ahead of him, the road is clear, so he steps harder on his accelerator. Ten seconds later he has passed the car and the speedometer shows 50 miles an hour, 73 feet per second. In those ten seconds the man has *changed* the rate of speed of his car twenty miles per hour, or he has accelerated his car at the rate of two miles per hour per second, or three feet per second per second.

Parachutes

An object falling off a cliff or out of an airplane is accelerated by gravity at a rate of 32 feet per second per second. This acceleration, due to gravity, is practically the same the world over. If you will, therefore, remember this figure of 32 feet per second per second and the rules that Newton worked out, you can figure for yourself the speed of any falling object, or the distance it has fallen in a given time.

The speed of any falling object is obtained simply by multiplying its gravity acceleration by the length of time it has fallen. After one second, the speed of a falling bomb or parachutist is 32 feet per second (32 × 1). At the end of ten seconds, if the object hasn't hit the ground, its speed will be 320 feet per second (32 × 10). You can thus see that objects keep falling faster and faster due to this acceleration of gravity.

To find the distance that an object has fallen, a little more mathematics is involved. The formula for this is

$$D = \tfrac{1}{2}g\, t^2$$

In this formula D is the distance an object has fallen; g stands for gravity acceleration—32 feet per second

TIME	VELOCITY PER SECOND	TOTAL DISTANCE
1 SECOND	32 FEET	16 FEET
2 "	64 "	64 "
3 "	96 "	144 "
4 "	128 "	256 "
5 "	160 "	400 "
6 "	192 "	576 "
7 "	224 "	784 "

THIS MAN IS FALLING VERTICALLY, GAINING SPEED BECAUSE OF THE PULL OF GRAVITY (NEGLECTING AIR RESISTANCE)

per second; *t* stands for time. If you understand algebra this simple formula is quite clear. If not, just a word of explanation: The t^2 means time squared or time multiplied by itself. Two seconds squared will be four seconds (2×2); three seconds squared will be nine seconds (3×3), etc. The distance an object has fallen will be $\frac{1}{2} \times 32 \times$ time, multiplied by itself. A pilot jumping from a stratosphere plane at the end of ten seconds will have fallen $\frac{1}{2} \times 32 \times 10 \times 10$ feet or 1,600 feet. A man falling from the highest point ever reached by an airplane would gain enough speed to hit the ground in just about a minute.

If these objects or people drop from a cliff, a balloon, or anything stationary, they would fall straight to the ground. If, however, they were dropped from an airplane that was moving forward, these objects would continue to move forward even after they left the airplane. This is hard to picture in your mind, but is absolutely true. The pull of gravity, drawing an object to the earth, acts independently of any other motion that the object will have. Just as an

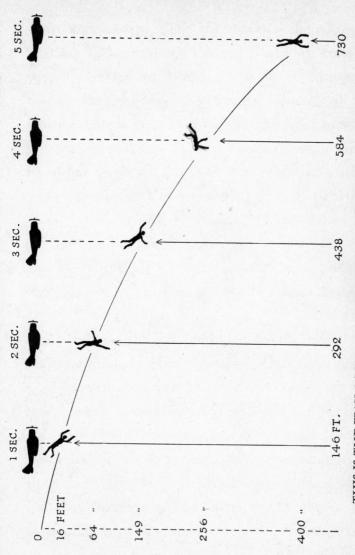

THIS IS THE WAY A MAN WOULD FALL IF HE JUMPED FROM A PLANE
GOING 100 MILES PER HOUR AND IF THERE WERE NO AIR RESISTANCE

example, let us suppose a parachutist leaps from a plane, traveling 100 miles per hour (146 feet per second). We are still ignoring the existence of the air. Where will he be at the end of one second? As soon as he left the plane, gravity started to pull him downward. Using our formula $D = \frac{1}{2}g\,t^2$, we find that our man has fallen only 16 feet during the first second, but during this time he has maintained his forward speed and has moved forward 146 feet. He could look up and see the plane 16 feet above his head. A second later he will have fallen 64 feet but will have traveled another 146 feet forward. If he is looking up, the 100 mile per hour plane will still be above him. At the end of the third second he will be 144 feet below the plane. At the end of the fourth second he is still below the plane, 256 feet down and nearly 600 feet ahead of the place where he jumped. When the chutist finally hits the ground, if he looks up the plane will be overhead. All the time he has been falling he has been traveling forward at the rate of 100 miles per hour.

Our parachutist gets down to earth and we must join him because all this time we have been talking

Sovfoto

THIS RUSSIAN PARACHUTIST FELL ABOUT 16 FEET THE FIRST SECOND. IF HE HAD NOT
PULLED THE RIP CORD, HIS RATE OF FALL WOULD

as though the air didn't exist. To look back over this chapter it does seem a bit unreal. If the air didn't exist there could be no airplanes and no parachutes. Yet it is important to realize that under these ideal conditions falling objects would behave as we have just described them. The fact that the air does exist modifies and limits the way a falling object behaves. But basically what we have just said still holds true. The air acts as a terrific brake or resistance to objects moving through it. We will consider very shortly just what effect the air has. Nevertheless, falling objects do increase in speed as they fall. If an object is moving forward when it falls, it continues to do so as it falls.

Chapter Seven

AIR RESISTANCE

EVEN now we are not prepared to face the question of how the air affects falling bodies and parachutes. We must stop a while longer to discuss air. The air is never static: winds blow, air currents shift, the pressure and amount of moisture in the air differ with the time and place. You already know that the air changes greatly with the altitude, especially in its upper limits. All of these factors make it inaccurate to talk about an object falling through the air, without mentioning exactly what part of the air we mean; just how the wind is blowing; and many other conditions.

To get around this difficulty in the study of air, scientists talk about a perfect or standard atmosphere that is not all disturbed by winds and currents. It is easier to describe things happening in a standard atmosphere, bearing in mind that actually the air will always be a little different than the standard atmosphere.

When two objects are in contact and in motion, there is friction between them. This may be a wheel on a road, a boat plowing through the ocean, or a parachutist falling through the air. Motion, of course, means speed and you can easily see that friction and speed are closely related. The faster an object moves through the air the more friction it creates. The more friction it creates, the more the object is slowed down. Friction increases with the square of the speed. If the speed doubles, four times as much friction is created. When a parachutist makes a delayed jump, that is, a jump where the rip cord is not pulled immediately, the pull of gravity will cause him to fall faster and faster each second. But the faster he falls, the more friction he creates moving through the air. Very soon these two forces will balance. Gravity

THE CANOPY INCREASES AIR RESISTANCE AND SLOWS THE
JUMPER'S SPEED TO ABOUT 18 FEET PER SECOND

makes him go faster, friction makes him go slower. When the balance point of these two forces is reached the man will fall at a steady speed.

This is what actually happens. During the first second the parachutist falls about 16 feet; during the second second about 48 feet. As he falls faster, friction begins to take effect. By the time he has fallen for about twelve seconds, he has reached a speed of 175 feet per second (120 miles per hour). At that speed friction balances gravity acceleration. No matter how much more the parachutist falls, he doesn't fall any faster. These figures are for an average weight parachutist. A lighter or heavier man would fall a little slower or faster at this terminal speed. If the parachutist begins to somersault, the resistance is increased and the terminal speed is slowed down to about 160 feet per second.

The balance between friction and gravity produces a constant rate of fall only in a constant medium, but the air is never constant. It is much denser and heavier at sea level than it is at higher altitudes. This density is closely tied up with friction. As the air becomes denser near sea level, an object falling through it produces greater friction. At high altitudes where the density of the air is less, friction is less. Consequently the speed at which the forces balance will be higher. A parachutist making a delayed jump from an altitude of about 20,000 feet would fall faster and faster until the drag of friction results in a constant speed. But even this constant speed would not really be constant. As the parachutist comes nearer to the earth he passes into denser air. Friction is increased and his terminal speed is gradually slowed down. Of course, he opens his chute before the air reaches the maximum density and from then on new problems are involved.

This density of the air is of considerable importance. If the air were much denser than it is now, it might be possible to get along without a parachute altogether. The increased friction, as a parachutist fell, might be enough to make him land at a safe speed even without help. Were the atmosphere on the earth less dense, parachutes would have to be much larger to break a man's fall, and perhaps they could not be used at all.

The function of the parachute is to increase greatly

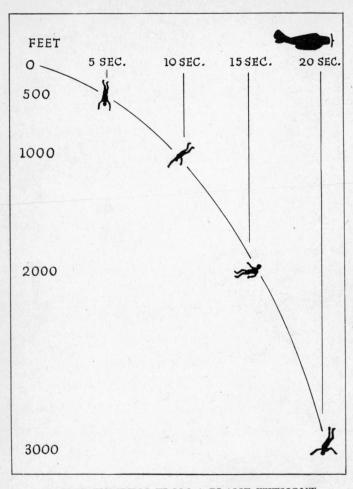

A MAN JUMPING FROM A PLANE WITHOUT
A PARACHUTE FALLS 3,000 FEET IN 20 SEC-
ONDS

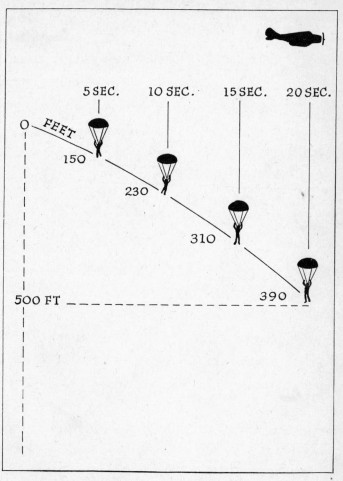

A MAN JUMPING FROM A PLANE WITH A
PARACHUTE FALLS ONLY 390 FEET IN 20
SECONDS

the resistance of a man who is falling. The resistance
is increased so much that the friction produced slows
down his terminal speed to one at which he can land
on the ground without injury. This effect is almost
entirely due to the increased area represented by the
parachute's canopy. If a man jumped head first from
a plane and continued to fall in that position, like a
high diver off a platform, his body would offer little
resistance as the air would press directly on only
about two square feet of body surface. If he jumped
from a prone position and fell in the same way, a
maximum of about ten square feet of body surface
might offer resistance to the air. Even this amount
would not slow a man down to a safe terminal speed.

As soon as our falling man pulls the rip cord of
the standard parachute he is wearing, the area offering resistance to the air is increased by 450 square
feet. This 450 square feet of silk is arranged in a
form that gives maximum resistance, as it moves
through the air. The inverted cup-shape offers resistance about one and a half times as great as that
of a flat surface the same diameter. The resistance
of the open parachute almost immediately slows down

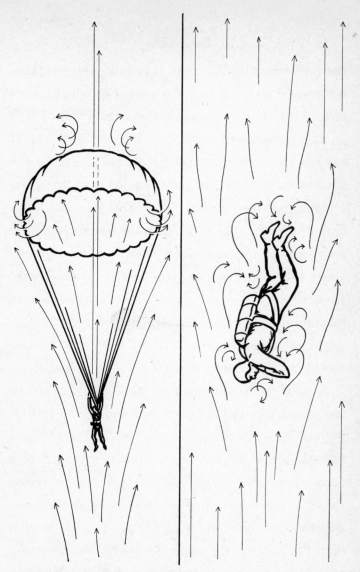

THIS GIVES A GENERAL IDEA OF AIR CUR-
RENTS AROUND A PARACHUTIST AFTER AND
BEFORE HE PULLS THE RIP CORD

the rate of descent to approximately 16 feet per second. The shock of landing at this speed is about the equivalent of jumping from a five-foot wall.

When a pilot or parachute trooper jumps from a plane he has a rapid forward motion as well as a downward motion. If he opens his chute immediately, the slipstream from the propeller will blow the chute open behind him. If he is making a delayed jump he will still be traveling forward and, as he opens his chute, it will pull out *behind* him rather than above him. The parachute, as it opens, checks the forward motion of the parachutist as well as his downward motion. As these two motions are checked and greatly reduced, the parachutist swings into place below the open canopy and falls steadily downward thereafter.

Because the parachutist is moving at great speed, there is a tremendous strain on the parachute at the moment it first opens. The total force acting on the parachute at this instant depends on the speed of the plane from which the man jumped, his weight, the distance he has fallen, the altitude, and other factors. The strain on a parachute produced by a man jumping from a 100 mile per hour plane and opening his

WIND FROM THE PROPELLERS AND THE FORWARD MOTION OF THE JUMPER MAKE THE CHUTE OPEN BEHIND HIM. AS HIS MOTION IS RETARDED, HE SWINGS INTO POSITION BE-LOW THE CHUTE

chute almost immediately is estimated to be about 500 pounds. Since the parachute is designed to take a strain of more than 2,500 pounds safely, nothing will break when the chute snaps open. The fact that the parachutist is supported by four harness belts distributes the shock, so that he is not injured. Even if the jump were from a plane going at 200 miles per hour or faster, there is little chance that the chute or the jumper would be injured by the strain of the chute's opening. The sudden shock may cause the jumper to "black out" for a second, but even this is not a real source of danger.

As the inverted cup-shaped chute falls it drags a mass of air along within it. This compresses the air and increases its pressure against the parachute. Air is forced out and "spills" on all sides of the chute. One column of air passes directly up through the chute and out through the vent hole at the apex. The pressure created by this vertical column of air tends to hold the chute steady. It reduces the oscillations that were so serious in the earliest types of parachutes. If oscillations do cause the chute to sway from side to side, the chutist can control them by pulling on the shroud lines opposite to the direction in which he is swinging.

The air is never still, as the parachute falls through it. If the air is moving horizontally the result is a wind that may carry the parachute several miles before it finally reaches the ground. Under certain conditions this may be dangerous. Aviators have been carried out to sea, into swamps, or up against buildings by the force of wind. Wind also increases the landing shock. Most bruises, sprains, and fractures that occur during parachute landings are the result of ground wind.

In addition to wind, there are vertical movements of the air that affect the parachute. Upward air currents may slow down the rate of descent and may actually cause the parachute to function as a sail, lifting the man up instead of dropping him down. Sergeant Moore of the Army Air Corps was caught in such a current when he made a jump from 2,000 feet. Normally he should have hit the ground in a minute and a half, but the upward current kept him in the air for 20 minutes, thus making his jump the slowest on record. Downward currents, on the other hand, will hasten his fall and may make his landing more dangerous. In his first jump with a hand-operated parachute, Leslie Irvin was caught in one of these down currents, and broke an ankle in landing.

Even when landing the parachutist's troubles with the air movements are not over. He must be sure to land facing the wind and leaning forward. If he does not land correctly, the canopy, now acting as a sail, will pull him over backward and drag him over the ground. Very probably the force of landing will knock the jumper off his feet. He learns to somersault quickly and recover his balance before the wind can upset him further. As soon as he is on his feet again, the chutist pulls the shroud lines to one side of the chute, emptying the air from the canopy and causing it to collapse. Not until he has the canopy gathered up and safely tucked away, is he free from the danger of ground winds.

It is the air resistance that makes the parachute possible. The careful balance of weight, area, and density of the air produce a rate of fall that will not result in serious injury to the jumper. Landing at 20 feet per second or faster is not safe unless one has

been trained to reduce the shock and to get the parachute under control immediately. This training is especially important for paratroops, who must land
quickly and get into action just as soon as possible
after they hit the ground. This is why their training
includes a great deal of gymnastics and practice in
landing.

Chapter Eight

HIGH ALTITUDES

THE call of the upper air was first a call of adventure. Planes soared higher and higher for the sake of establishing altitude records. With these attempts came a period of exploration that proved man could use the upper air. Long distance flights were speeded up by the lessened air resistance and by the more even atmospheric conditions at high altitudes. Then came the war. In order to have full advantage over the enemy it was essential to climb fast, maneuver over the enemy planes, and dive down with guns wide open. The flying ceiling rose higher and higher. With the aid of super-

98

chargers to supply air for the motors, planes could be effective at 25,000, 30,000 and 35,000 feet above the ground.

Conditions at these altitudes are so different from those on the surface that they are hard for us to imagine. As the plane climbs, the temperature falls lower and lower until at 35,000 feet it is well below zero. The pressure falls at an increasing rate. By the time the plane reaches 18,000 feet it has gone through half of the air.

The following table shows changes in the air with increases in height:

Air Conditions and Altitude

(Standard Atmosphere)

Altitude (feet)	Temperature (C.)	Relative Pressure	Relative Density
0	15	1.0	1.0
5,000	5	.83	.86
10,000	—5	.67	.74
15,000	—15	.56	.63
20,000	—25	.46	.53
25,000	—45	.30	.37

The rarefied atmosphere cannot support wings as well. The plane's ascent is slowed up. The motor doesn't draw in enough oxygen at each stroke to provide for complete combustion of the gasoline. It becomes less and less efficient. Without the supercharger to force an extra supply of air into the cylinders a plane could not maintain itself at these heights. Altitude brings other sources of danger. A few drops of water in the gasoline will instantly freeze and clog the fuel pipe. The cold affects the lubrication, the instruments, and the controls.

The conquest of the upper air was not made without loss of life. It took time to learn how to overcome the obstacles of low temperature and pressure. Even the pilot is affected by altitude. He must wear special warm clothing, often electrically heated, to guard against the cold. He must take care that his goggles do not freeze over and blind him. But most of all he fears anoxia—lack of oxygen due to low pressure.

At sea level the pilot takes in about a pint of air at each breath. Of that pint of air about one-fifth is oxygen. Part of this oxygen is absorbed by the pilot's lungs. It helps furnish the energy he needs for flying. At 18,000 feet his breath takes in about half

PLANES ARE PENETRATING HIGHER AND HIGHER INTO THE THIN COLD AIR. THE DANGER
OF JUMPING FROM THESE HEIGHTS HAS BEEN CAREFULLY STUDIED

the amount of air and half the amount of oxygen—not enough to keep him going.

As he climbs above 15,000 feet the pilot opens the valve of his oxygen tank and adjusts the oxygen mask. Now he is equipped to get oxygen at any altitude. As long as he breathes from the tank he is safe. Should anything go wrong, he would suffocate from lack of oxygen as certainly as a man drowning. Effects of anoxia are not felt suddenly. The pilot may become light-headed, then dizzy, nauseous, and drowsy. He may struggle to keep awake and find it hard to keep his eyes open and his hands active at the controls. He may then become unconscious. However, a few pilots have survived this experience. When they lost control of their plane, it dived rapidly back toward the earth and the denser air. The increased oxygen in the lower air enabled the pilots to recover consciousness in time to gain control of their plane before landing.

Slowly the upper air was conquered. Planes were improved. The pilots were protected by improved oxygen masks and electric heaters. As these problems were overcome one by one, new ones arose that had to be mastered. Would a parachute work at these heights? How could a pilot breathe once his chute had opened at 30,000 feet? Aviation and medical experts got together again to tackle the problems.

Doctors from the Mayo Clinic, Northwestern University Medical School and scientists from several universities set out to experiment. They used a large air-tight tank from which pumps could quickly remove the air till the pressure dropped to that of any desired height. Volunteers in the tank were under the same conditions as pilots at high altitudes. These men risked their lives to try new oxygen masks. They worked out a way to switch from the oxygen tank of the plane to a pocket-sized oxygen tank that the pilot could carry with him. This switch had to be made quickly and accurately. A delay of less than half a minute or an error produced unconsciousness. An unconscious pilot at 30,000 feet is extremely close to death.

The volunteers made field tests. Each took up with him a small tank of oxygen. Into this tiny tank, 38 quarts of oxygen had been compressed. When the valve was opened, the oxygen was released at the rate of two quarts a minute into the respirator. The amount of oxygen was carefully computed in advance. Experiments determined. the rate at which oxygen was used in breathing. Two quarts a minute was ample.

Suppose the pilot jumped at 30,000 feet. He would then have to fall through 12,000 feet of rarefied air till he would reach the safe 18,000-foot level. A standard parachute falls at about 16 feet per second; perhaps a bit faster up where the air offers less resistance. This is close to 1,000 feet per minute—12 minutes for the 12,000-foot fall to safety. At two quarts per minute, the tank of oxygen will supply the pilot for full 19 minutes—more than enough to get him to a safe level. Besides this, the pilot may fall some distance before his chute opens—this makes the time to reach the 18,000-foot level even shorter. The tank of oxygen is sufficient to save any pilot jumping below 40,000 feet.

Temperature is also a problem, but the pilot's warm clothes are sufficient for the short time he is falling in the extremely cold regions. As he falls the temperature becomes warmer and, even in winter, the chances of severe frostbite are small.

Now parachutists were ready to try the upper atmosphere in earnest. James Nieland, a French parachutist, desired to break the Russian delayed drop record. Because he was not sure of the effects of high altitude, Nieland secured the co-operation of several doctors and submitted to tests in a decompression or altitude chamber. Air was pumped from the tank, temperatures were lowered until the effect was similar to that at high altitudes. Nieland reported his reactions through a telephone connection. Instruments strapped to his body measured heartbeat and breathing. Air was returned to the chamber at rates equal to the experience of falling earthward at speeds up to 300 feet per second. Nieland went through these tests with no important ill effect, so actual field tests were begun.

Equipped with medical instruments, oxygen, and two parachutes, Nieland made three jumps; the highest from about 37,000 feet. Doctors checked him carefully before and after the jumps and concluded that these long delayed jumps were not harmful. However, by the next year the delayed jump record was again broken by a Russian. News of Nieland's experiments did not reach this country till some time later.

The Russians pushed higher and higher for parachute records. In August, 1940, the chutist Kharokhonov bailed out at 40,813 feet. This was a delayed drop. Kharokhonov had his hand on the rip cord but did not pull. The oxygen respirator worked perfectly, but the jumper lost a glove and nearly froze his hand. However, he was falling fast. He spun round and round. The gray earth began to look green. Landmarks became visible. The seconds passed and finally Kharokhonov pulled the rip cord, 2,100 feet above ground. A few seconds later he pulled the cord of his emergency chute to slow him down still more and shortly after he was safe on the earth again.

Back home in the United States, Arthur Starnes, a veteran parachutist, had an idea. Sometimes an idea comes like a flash, sometimes it slowly grows and takes form. Starnes, who had been parachuting since 1924, gradually became more and more interested in delayed jumps. He had made a number of delayed jumps; first 2,500 feet, then more and more up to

35 MILES

RAREFIED ATMOSPHERE

25 "

HIGHEST UNMANNED BALLOON

15 "

HIGHEST PLANE RECORD 14 MILES

HIGHEST MANNED BALLOON

STRATOSPHERE - - - - - - - - - - - - - - - - - -

HIGHEST PARACHUTE JUMP
7 MILES

MT. EVEREST
29,002 FT.

5 "

SEA LEVEL

JUMPS HAVE NOT YET BEEN MADE FROM
THE HIGHEST ALTITUDES REACHED BY AIR-
PLANES

9,000. These jumps proved to Starnes that delayed jumping was safe. He did not lose consciousness; he suffered no injury. The possibility of better and higher delayed jumps intrigued him.

There was reason for his interest. Planes were pushing up the ceiling. Sooner or later men would have to jump from great heights. Speed was rapidly increasing. What would be the dangers of a chute opening at a 200 or 300 mile speed? Starnes thought these questions over. He knew that the terminal speed of a falling man is not more than 130 miles per hour. The resistance of the air keeps him from falling any faster. A pilot jumping from a 200 mile per hour plane would also have the same 200 mile velocity. If he opened his chute immediately, the shock of braking from 200 miles per hour to 12 miles per hour might be severe. If the pilot held back and did not pull his rip cord, the air resistance would soon slow down his fall and after a bit the pilot would be falling at 120 or 130 miles per hour instead of 200 or more. If the chute is opened at this time, the shock will be distinctly less.

Starnes reasoned that delayed jumps might be a

IF A PILOT JUMPING AT HIGH ALTITUDE OPENS HIS CHUTE
IMMEDIATELY, HE MAY SUFFER FROM COLD AND LACK OF
OXYGEN BEFORE REACHING A SAFE LEVEL

good thing—if they would only work. It was then that Starnes' idea crystallized. Why not make experimental high altitude delayed jumps so arranged that the safety of such a measure could be completely proved?

In 1930 Starnes started talking about this idea, although very few people listened. Time went on and in 1938 he tried again. The year following, others became interested and by 1940 scientists at the University of Chicago and Northwestern University Medical School were ready to co-operate.

Meantime the Second World War had started. This was a different war. It was fast, desperate, and merciless. Pilots bailing out of crippled planes were shot by the enemy as they floated slowly down to earth. It looked as if the parachute might become a death trap rather than a life saver. But there was a way out—the delayed drop. The pilot who waited till he was near ground before he yanked the rip cord had a much better chance than one who pulled the cord at 20,000 feet. Delayed jumps had a purpose and a test of delayed jumping became important.

The experiments got under way. This was not

merely a matter of making a jump from a high altitude. It was not an attempt to break a record, but an experiment to discover the effects of high altitude delayed jumps on the parachutist. Starnes prepared for his jump with instruction and tests in a decompression chamber. He learned how to use the oxygen mask and how to release pressure in his ears. Doctors studied his heart and breathing under these artificial conditions before plans for the field tests were finally made.

Because this was an experiment, Starnes carried with him a variety of scientific apparatus so the records would be complete. This apparatus varied in weight from 80 to 100 pounds. It made jumping more difficult and the extra weight increased Starnes' terminal velocity when falling. Five preliminary jumps were made. In these the distance of free fall was 9,500 to 11,300 feet before the rip cord was pulled. Apparatus was tested, records were made, and everything was prepared for a final and last jump to terminate the project.

For the final jump Starnes was well prepared. He wore an electrically heated flying suit, heavy gloves, boots, and a helmet to which earphones, goggles, and an oxygen mask were attached. Mounted on his chest was a pneumograph to record his breathing; a microphone and transmitter to send out a record of heartbeats; a recording barometer; a stopwatch; radio set, altimeter, and movie camera. Every item in his bulky load had a purpose; even the camera that photographed Starnes' body movements as he fell through the air. Arrangements were made to keep radio contact with the jumper as he fell.

The day of the jump came. The plane went aloft carrying Starnes and three assistants. The temperature dropped rapidly as the plane reached the cold upper air. The thermometer outside the cabin reached 30 degrees below zero and no longer recorded the temperature. Electric heaters warmed the interior of the plane to approximately zero. A careful timing schedule had been worked out in advance. Starnes had to have everything ready before he jumped. The plane reached an altitude of 30,800 feet. Starnes' timer counted off the seconds. Recording devices were started, oxygen turned on. As the last second ticked off, Starnes grasped the open door and jumped.

As Starnes jumped, a short cord attached to the plane automatically started the stopwatch. Later, when he pulled the rip cord, the opening chute stopped the watch and in this way the time of the free fall was accurately measured at 116.5 seconds.

Starnes fell fast, through air nearly 50 degrees below zero. As he turned he saw the plane pass above him. He soon reached his terminal velocity—228 miles per hour and then slowed down as he came into denser air. The recording instruments were at work. Seconds were going by. Starnes' goggles froze solid as he plunged through high clouds. He spun around, fell back first, then feet first, but all the time he was fully conscious and knew exactly what he was doing and what was going on. Soon he raised his goggles for a peek at his altimeter—he had already fallen halfway. Starnes watched the needle slowly drop from 15,000 feet where the air was warmer and safe to breathe down to 10,000, and still the needle moved down.

Starnes had fallen for well over a minute. Everything was going well; the experiment was a success. The altimeter needle passed the 2,000-foot mark.

Starnes tightened his grip on the rip cord and pulled. The chute opened with a jerk that caused the jumper to "blackout" momentarily. A few seconds later he recovered and opening his smaller emergency chute, drifted to a safe landing.

The jump was over, but the experiment was not. Records had to be checked, their meaning made clear. The stopwatch showed that Starnes had fallen for one minute and 56 seconds. His average speed was 170 miles per hour. During the fall he breathed fourteen times. Each breath was completely recorded and each heartbeat was, too. Mentally, Starnes was alert and active. He watched his instruments, noted air conditions and his own feelings.

The study of records is still incomplete, but it shows that jumps from high altitude may be made with comparative safety. There is no undue strain on the heart. The jumper's mind is clear and alert, perhaps more so than if he were on the ground. Records have given information about body position and speed of fall, and have thrown light on the problem of "blackout." Aviators need not fear high altitude jumps and long free falls. Starnes had the opportunity to test his idea, and aviation is indebted to him and to the medical men who carried through with the experiment.

Chapter Nine

CATERPILLAR CLUB

IN the air corps, pilots do not spend much time studying the parachute or practicing jumps. Each pilot carries a parachute, just as each sailor in dangerous waters wears his life preserver. If the pilot must use the chute he has to use it properly the first time—or he doesn't get a chance to try again.

Because the parachute is primarily a life saver, the most interesting and dramatic stories about parachutes are those that directly concern people who have been snatched from death as their chute opened. These dramatic stories teem with narrow escapes and individual heroism. The tales told by the men who have lived to tell them are worth repeating.

On October 20, 1922, Lieutenant Harris saved his life when the plane he was testing broke up over McCook Field. This first life-saving jump from a plane proved the reliability of the hand-operated parachute. It also attracted a good deal of attention and newspapers gave the story (already told in this book) wide publicity.

Some members of the parachute unit secured photographs of Lieutenant Harris and his wrecked plane. These and souvenirs from the wreck were used to decorate a wall in the laboratory at McCook Field. Visitors always stopped to look over the display and two of them, both newspapermen, suggested that a club be formed of aviators who saved their lives by parachute. The idea was discussed but nothing happened, until M. H. St. Clair, a parachute engineer, who had taken part in the discussion, received a tractor advertisement that suggested the name "caterpillar."

St. Clair was so enthusiastic over the name, which seemed appropriate because the parachute is made of silk, that he called in the newspapermen and they too agreed. Within a month after Lieutenant Harris jumped, the Caterpillar Club was organized. Perhaps "organized" is not the right word because the club has no real organization: it has no president, or secretary, no club rooms, or dues. In reality the Caterpillar Club is nothing more than a record kept at the office of the U. S. Army Air Corps. It is just a list of names. But each name on the list represents a person who saved his life by jumping from a disabled plane with a parachute. The U. S. Army Air Corps merely acts as custodian of the record and verifies the claim of candidates who desire to be added to the list.

Lieutenant Harris was put down as Caterpillar Number 1, but search of records revealed that there were undoubtedly many others who might be listed before him. The club had five members in 1922, 27 in 1925, 120 in 1928, and well over 200 in 1930. Since then the list has grown at even a faster rate. If the club is extended to a world-wide organization it would be difficult to estimate how many thousands of members should be enrolled at this time.

The total membership of the Caterpillar Club does

Official Photograph, U. S. Army Air Corps

A PERFECT LANDING BY A TRAINED PARATROOPER AT FORT
BENNING, GA.

not include all the people whose lives have been saved by chutes. Only those who have leaped from a disabled aircraft are entitled to membership. The professional jumper or paratrooper whose main chute fails to open and who saves his life by means of the emergency chute is not a true Caterpillar. Jumping is part of their business and part of the risk they take.

After the Caterpillar Club was organized in 1922, the story of an amazing rescue, three years before, was added to its annals. In July, 1919, the Goodyear Rubber Company assembled a 150-foot blimp in an amusement park near Chicago. This aircraft was commissioned to make a good will tour over the Middle West. The bag was filled with 90,000 cubic feet of inflammable hydrogen. Below it hung a gondola supporting two 80 horsepower motors.

That eventful afternoon the blimp made two short test flights and then took on passengers for a third. One of them was a newspaper reporter. There were parachutes on board, but they were not worn by the crew. Everything was ready. The photographer unlimbered his camera, the ground crew cast off, and the *Wingfoot Express* nosed upwards. As she gained altitude, Boettner, the pilot, headed her over Chicago at about 1,500 feet. It was late afternoon. Homebound workers stopped to gaze at the roaring cigar that floated above. Suddenly there was a burst of flame; a back-firing motor had ignited the canvas and the inflammable gas inside it. Boettner shouted orders. The men grabbed their parachute harness, struggled into it and jumped. Four were able to clear the burning mass and leaped for safety. The flaming bag collapsed and plunged toward the ground. Flames from the bag set one of the descending chutes on fire. The jumper was killed. The other chutes drifted aside. Boettner's canopy too was ignited, but he climbed the shroud lines and beat out the flames. The blazing blimp struck the roof of a bank, crashing through and exploding its gasoline tanks. People in the bank were burned alive.

Meantime the three parachutists approached the rooftops. One struck the side of a building and fell to the street, fatally injured. Boettner and one of his mechanics were injured in landing, but survived. In all, thirteen people were killed and thirty injured. It was only fitting that Boettner and Wacker, the two survivors from the blimp, should head the list of Caterpillars.

Another thrilling Caterpillar tale tells of chute number 28-8. It saved the lives of three different men. Not one chute in fifty ever gets used in an emergency, but 28-8 was lucky. On June 18, 1929, Lieutenant Harberger of the air corps wore 28-8 when he took a new plane up for a test. The plane went into a spin and did not recover. Flames burst from the motor. Less than 1,000 feet from the ground Harberger leaped from the cockpit, pulled the rip cord, and landed safely.

Three months later young Howard Poyas was wearing the same chute in a commercial plane. Poyas did night flying with a neon light advertisement under his wings. High over Los Angeles the motor began to knock and went dead. Poyas headed for open country, rapidly losing altitude. As he reached the outskirts of Los Angeles, he realized the time had come. He dove through an open window of his cabin and landed safely in a vacant lot. The plane crashed into a hillside.

In November of the same year, pilot P. G. Stevens

PARATROOPERS WEAR TWO CHUTES, ONE FOR EMERGENCY
USE. THESE MEN ARE NOT ELIGIBLE FOR THE CATERPILLAR
CLUB

wore the 28-8 up in a biplane. Suddenly the ship began to lose altitude and went into a spin. Stevens
pulled it out. Again it started spinning, and again the
pilot brought it around safely. But when the plane
went into a nose dive, Stevens decided to jump. Just

then the plane looped and threw Stevens from the cockpit. He grabbed the rip cord and pulled. A while later he landed easily, gathered up his chute, and started in search of his wrecked plane.

Every pilot has faith in his parachute. He knows it will open when he needs it. But it took a man like Fanrik Billing to show how complete that faith could be. Billing, a member of the Swedish Royal Air Force, was scheduled for stunt flying at an air exhibit near Stockholm. At the signal, the light plane tore down the runway and into the air. As it left the ground, Billing sensed that something was wrong. He circled back and saw, to his horror, that the wheels of his landing gear were rolling on the runway below. Billing knew that landing without a severe crack-up was now impossible.

The crowd at the exhibit strained to see what would happen. They saw the tiny plane climb. Then followed a series of loops, spins, and stunts. Billing was going right through his program as if nothing had happened. People wondered if Billing was aware of the trouble. He was, but he knew his chute was ready whenever he wanted to use it. After his per-

LANDING IN WATER IS MORE HAZARDOUS THAN HITTING
GROUND. THIS RUSSIAN JUMPER IS SLIPPING OUT OF HIS
HARNESS

formance, Billing climbed the plane up almost out of sight. Soon it reappeared in a steep dive, headed toward a nearby lake. The crowd watched the plane tear down and plunge into the water—but Billing was not in it. He bailed out as soon as he was certain no one would be injured in the crash, and was slowly coming down in his chute. No member of the Caterpillar Club got a warmer reception when he landed.

Test pilots have important but dangerous work to do. It is not surprising to find a number of their names in the roll of the Caterpillar Club. In the early days of the supercharger, Lieutenant Haddon was assigned to test one on a pursuit plane. Haddon took off and climbed steadily upward. The air grew colder. As he passed 18,000 feet he opened his oxygen tank and breathed in oxygen through a rubber tube. The cold increased. By 32,000 feet it was 50 below zero. This made breathing difficult. As he drove his plane higher and higher, Haddon was overcome by the cold and lack of oxygen. He lost consciousness. The tube slipped from between his lips. His plane roared down toward the earth. As it entered the denser air, Haddon revived. When his eyes came to focus he saw that his altimeter registered only 9,000 feet. The motor knocked badly. It practically stopped. Haddon took control, but the ship lost altitude and the motor burst into flames. He tried the fire extinguisher but this didn't help. He had to jump while there was sufficient altitude. In a few seconds Haddon floated free of the burning ship, landed safely, and walked to a nearby farmhouse to phone in his report.

There is a wealth of adventure in the records of the Caterpillar Club, enough to fill several books. There you will find the record of Captain Gray's balloon ascent to 42,000 feet and his parachute escape from his falling balloon. Also the story of the plane full of fireworks that exploded over Nashville. You will read of collisions, of struggles with ice, of rescues at sea. In every case the canopy of silk saved the pilot from certain death.

In wartime, the parachute has become even more important as a life preserver. But because it is wartime, details of the exploits are not publicized. According to one reliable source, 85% of the British flyers shot down over England during the mass air raids of 1940 parachuted to safety.

Chapter Ten

PARACHUTES IN RUSSIA

WE Americans do things in a big way and we are proud of it. We build the tallest buildings and the largest dams. We have more automobiles, bathtubs, telephones than any other country in the world. But when it comes to parachutes, we have to play second fiddle to Russia. The Russians have done a bigger and better job, and we should give them credit for it. There is no doubt that we might have done as good a job if we had set about doing it. The fact remains, however, that we did not. Russia's use of chutes is such a success story that it calls for serious attention.

Russia did not have an easy time of it at the end of the last World War. Inside her borders were war, famine, and revolution. Outside, people were suspicious and hostile. In the years of struggle that followed, establishing Soviet power and industry, there was little time for airplanes or parachutes. In fact, ten years passed before the first parachute jump was made in Russia. The first jump took place in 1927. It was made by the now famous pilot Gromov, who thereby saved his life.

Parachutes were not completely foreign to Russia before that time. Records show that as far back as 1911, one G. E. Kotelnikov, an inventor, experimented with parachute designs. His efforts were rejected by the commander of the Czar's air corps, who argued that a parachute would tempt the pilot to leap at any sign of trouble without regard for his plane.

At the sports festival in July, 1930, the Russian people had their first look at a new sport—parachute jumping. A group of hardy young men and women gave an exhibition of jumping from planes. They were neither pilots nor professionals but young factory workers who had taken up parachuting, in their spare time, for the sport itself. They had contests to see who could land nearest a chosen spot. Parachute jumping became a new and exciting pastime.

The idea spread and more clubs were formed in schools and factories. In three years these were so numerous they were taken over by a central organization. This central organization, known as Osoaviakhim (the Society for the Promotion of Aviation and Chemical Defense), might best be described as a cross between a civil defense corps and an athletic union. Its purpose is to aid the air and chemical defense of Russia. There are divisions pertaining to chemical warfare, gas, decontaminations, and rescue. Other divisions work with gliders, planes, and balloons. In 1933 the Osoaviakhim took over the parachute clubs and organized them into a nationwide movement.

With this powerful organization behind it, the idea of parachuting spread like wild-fire. Almost every factory, farm, school, and village had its parachute club. All young people could enter—even those in high school. Training towers were built, parachute

OVER 500 TOWERS PROVIDE PARACHUTE TRAINING FOR
YOUNG PEOPLE IN RUSSIA

schools were started. Chutes and planes were made available. Leaders organized contests, exhibits and demonstrations.

Soon these young Russians were going after records. Altitude records were made and broken by men and women. So were records for delayed jumps, for accuracy in landing, for landing in water, and for jumping at night. On his 599th jump the Soviet hero, Kharokhonov, bailed out at 40,813 feet and fell headlong for 38,700 feet before opening his chute. This altitude and delayed drop record was made on August 24, 1940. Previous records were 36,201 feet and 27,880 feet for men. The women's record is 26,158 feet. The record mass jump, made by 29 men jumping together, was 23,000 feet.

The progress of the parachute clubs went on so rapidly that it is hard to grasp it. The first mass jump of parachutists took place on August 18, 1933. On that afternoon 62 young chutists jumped from three bombers and floated down to the admiring crowd below. In 1934, the year after parachuting became an official activity, 4,500 jumps from planes were reported and about 300,000 jumps from training towers. By 1935 the number of jumps from planes rose to 11,000 and from towers to 800,000. The next year the total came to 30,000 jumps from planes and 1,600,000 tower jumps. These figures only cover the civilians taking part in the training program. The army had a program of its own. More recent figures are not obtainable. A 1940 estimate puts the number of young people trained in parachute jumping at 1,000,000.

Chutes, equipment and training are provided free through the government-controlled Osoaviakhim. The young people gladly give their time to this popular sport. While the sport side has been emphasized, a great deal of the training becomes important in defense and in war. Map reading is part of the training; so are first aid and gymnastics. Groups practice mass jumps under sealed orders. They jump together over some objective a distance from the airport and reassemble after landing. The group leader opens the sealed orders and the party may find itself instructed to hike to a neighboring field for a home-bound plane. They may be instructed to "attack" some local objective, to "destroy" communications, or to map the region. Such training has proved invaluable.

When the World's Fair opened in New York in

1939 the 250-foot parachute tower with its colored chutes attracted widespread attention. It is estimated that over a million visitors paid for the thrill of going up and descending in a parachute to a safe landing. The large and spectacular tower was probably bigger than any the Russians built—but in 1936 there were 559 parachute training towers in Russia and 115 parachute training stations!

These training towers are of all shapes and sizes. Some are small wooden structures. Some are sizeable steel affairs. Every large park or recreation area tries to have one—just as we like to have a good baseball diamond. There were even smaller models for young children. These towers are a combination of a slide and jump. Boys and girls climb up 12 or 15 feet to the top of the slide and sit down on a small swinging seat. When released, the child slides down a few feet, then off into the air—and a controlled chute lowers him ten feet or so to the ground.

The parachute clubs encourage their members to experiment and improve their equipment. In 1938 the Doronin brothers perfected a type of automatic chute. The mechanism can be set to open the chute

PARACHUTISTS START YOUNG IN RUSSIA. THIS IS A MINIA-
TURE CHILDREN'S CHUTE WITH A 12-FOOT DROP

at any time from 5 to 180 seconds after the person jumps. Reports state that the chute was successfully used in over 200 jumps at altitudes from 3,000 to 15,000 feet with the chute timed to open from 5 to 60 seconds after leaving the plane.

The Red Army was also active at the same time that the civilian training program was growing so steadily. Troops parachuted to earth at the army maneuvers at Voronezh in August, 1930. This dramatic feat was so impressive it was repeated at Moscow a month later. By 1936 several hundred men were involved in the parachute maneuvers. The staff officers pronounced them a complete success. Shortly thereafter, near Moscow, clouds of parachutists came down into the fields. Five thousand two hundred men are supposed to have dropped on that occasion: infantrymen, artillery, and auxiliary fighters. Machine guns, anti-tank guns, and all sorts of equipment floated down to the earth. These impressive maneuvers were repeated the following year. In 1939 these parachute troops had their first test in battle.

Because the Russians are so interested in their parachutes, they are continually finding new uses for

MANY WOMEN ARE PARACHUTISTS IN RUSSIA. THIS GIRL
IS A NATIVE OF SIBERIA

them. On February 24, 1941, a squad of Russian
paratroopers dropped from planes into the snow-
covered mountains. Supply chutes followed with skis
and guns. The troops put on their skis and completed
successful maneuvers in an area that could not have
been easily reached otherwise. Not long after, our
own army began working on plans for ski paratroops.

We now have such groups trained for mountain fighting.

The Russians have a long northern frontier where the outposts are snowbound and isolated the greater part of the year. Now, with planes and chutes, mail and supplies can be delivered with regularity and the monotony of guarding an arctic outpost is broken by more frequent news and gifts from home.

The distances in Siberia have created other problems as well. It is difficult to provide medical attention to the widely scattered inhabitants. A doctor who must come by horse or dog sled may arrive too late, if he can travel at all. Now the government medical service is provided by air. Over 12,000 patients are treated yearly by doctors who come by plane. Even plane travel is limited because weather and ground conditions are often so bad that landings are impossible. In these cases, many of the young doctors and nurses parachute to an emergency case, carrying their supplies with them. One doctor has made over 200 jumps and has the satisfaction of knowing that the blood transfusions, operations, and treatments made possible by his visits have saved

Sovfot

IN FULL SCALE MILITARY MANEUVERS OVER 5,000 RUSSIAN
SOLDIERS SWEPT DOWN FROM THE SKIES

many lives.

The Russians, like our own Forest Service, are using chutes to land men and supplies for fighting forest fires. The forests of Siberia are in many ways similar to those of our Northwest and the same methods of fire fighting are applicable. The Russian crew consists of a pilot, an observer, and three or four jumpers. The men parachute near the fire. Supplies and equipment are sent after them in special chutes that lower the tools safely. If the region is more settled, a single fire fighter parachutes out. This man rounds up the local inhabitants and organizes them into an efficient fire fighting force. In the first year of this work, 1937, ninety fires were put out by parachuted rangers. The use of planes and chutes is now part of the routine forest patrol.

In the current war, not only troops, but doctors, nurses and guerrillas are dropped by chutes. Besides the men and women in active service, Russia probably has more reserves trained to use chutes than any other country or than all other countries combined. They have set a good example, one that we have been quick to follow.

Chapter Eleven

THE AMERICAN PARACHUTE ARMY

NEITHER a Russian expert nor a crafty Nazi first thought of the idea of parachute troops. Credit goes to an American —none other than our own Benjamin Franklin. Franklin was in France as our ambassador at the time when balloons were being perfected and parachutes first tried. In 1784 Franklin wrote the following advice: "Five thousand balloons capable of raising two men each could not cost more than five ships of the line; and where is the prince who can afford so to cover his country with troops for its defense as that ten thousand men descending from the clouds might not in many places do an infinite deal of mischief before a force could be brought together to repel them."

This sound advice of Franklin's went unheeded for a long time. But it is to our credit that the United States actually experimented with parachute troops even before Russia and Germany. Our General William Mitchell first conceived the idea of air-borne troops. The General was so enthusiastic that he arranged a demonstration. In October, 1928, a Martin bomber flew over Kelly Field in Texas. From it dropped the first six American "paratroopers." Their chutes opened and dropped them safely to the ground. Within three minutes after they had landed, the men had reassembled. Their machine gun was set up and ready for action. This was only a small scale demonstration and funds were lacking for further work. Officers viewing this successful demonstration were not impressed by the possibilities of this new form of attack. A report was filed at the War Department. There it was forgotten. General Mitchell continued his fruitless campaign for a powerful air force.

Because our renewed parachute program did not

U. S. PARACHUTISTS ARE SPECIALLY SELECTED AND TRAINED VOLUNTEERS

begin until May, 1940, we were able to profit by
lessons learned from abroad. Once experiments
showed that the idea of parachute troops was practical, a training program was set up. A steady stream
of expert parachutists has been coming from the
parachute schools ever since. Some of the trainees are

absorbed into the teaching staff of the school and, with an enlarged faculty, men are being trained at an ever increasing rate.

The experimental parachute platoon was organized at Fort Benning, Georgia, in May, 1940. This small group consisted of two officers and 48 enlisted men, whom Captain William T. Ryder selected from 200 volunteers. They had meager equipment, little experience, and no buildings of their own. Two months later, as part of their training, this group was brought to Hightstown, New Jersey, where Colonel J. H. Strong, who had built the parachute towers at the New York World's Fair, had constructed two 125-foot training towers. Unlike the Fair towers that thrilled the visitors, these at Hightstown had a more important job. At these towers the troopers learned the fundamentals of parachute jumping. The instructors watched the students in actual practice. They followed each trainee as his chute fell. Errors were corrected immediately. From the training towers to actual jumps from planes was only one step, and the job was done. The parachute platoon convincingly demonstrated its value and the organization of the first United States parachute battalion on October 3, 1940, was officially ordered. The same month requirements for personnel were sent out to army camps. This call brought a flood of volunteers. Nearly ten times as many applicants as could be accommodated during the first year's program, sent in their names.

The parachute battalions are composed entirely of volunteers. Only unmarried men may join. Jumping itself is not hazardous but the tasks to be performed by the paratroops when they land may be. Young unmarried men are, therefore, preferred. Volunteers are required to be between the ages of 21 and 32; height from 66 to 74 inches. Weight may vary with the height, but no soldier weighing over 185 pounds is accepted as a parachutist. The men must not only meet the usual army physical requirements but must be tough, steady, dependable, with nerves of iron.

The headquarters at Fort Benning were being completely rebuilt for the new battalion. New barracks were constructed, new classrooms, a training field was laid out, jumping platforms built. Above this new construction rose two gigantic training towers.

These new training towers were modeled after the ones at Hightstown but were twice their size. They rise 250 feet from the ground—higher than most tall buildings. One is constructed with eight guide cables onto which the parachute is hooked. The 32-foot parachute is raised by a cable and is automatically released when it hits the top. To the parachute is attached a wooden seat, holding two passengers. On this swinging seat, the training begins. The guide cables and braking devices control the chute so that it is perfectly safe. The second tower is more simply constructed: a large ring is lowered from the top to which the chute is attached. The advanced student is hauled up in a harness. At the right moment the chute is released and it floats freely to the earth. The student is on his own once the chute is free: he must guide it, control it, and land safely.

There is also a special device that gives the student the feel of dropping from an airplane. He is hoisted about 30 feet in the air in a prone position. At this height he releases himself and drops freely, just as he would if he leaped from a plane. When he has fallen 13 feet, the ropes attached to his harness tighten and

THESE SKI TROOPS HAVE BEEN TRAINED TO DROP BY PARA-
CHUTE. THEY CAN TAKE AND HOLD STRATEGIC MOUNTAIN
POSITIONS

he is yanked around to falling position with just the
same pull as if his parachute really opened.

The test parachute platoon formed a nucleus of
the 501st Battalion. Major W. M. Miley was put in
charge. He soon developed a group of hardened,

trained men. At the end of the six-week course, his paratroopers were completely trained to handle expertly their chutes and their weapons.

The staff of instructors grew to 9 officers and 47 men, fully equipped to train about 1,500 volunteers yearly. Facilities have been further increased and more men trained. The battalion reached its authorized strength far ahead of schedule. The 502nd Parachute Battalion was formed and the 503rd. With increased experience, the training of each new group of paratroopers becomes better and better. The flood of volunteers still continues. The aerial army has really begun to grow.

Colonel William C. Lee has been placed in charge of the enlarged army of paratroopers. Colonel Lee has not been nicknamed "the jumping Colonel" because he is an armchair executive. He is a jumper, too, and doesn't expect his men to do anything their officers can't. When placed in charge of the growing battalions, Colonel Lee was ill with influenza. As soon as he had sufficient strength to walk, he got into his flying clothes and up for a jump. With leaders like the Colonel, the program couldn't go wrong.

At the training school officers emphasize the fact that paratroops are fundamentally a branch of the infantry—not the air corps. The parachute helps men get into positions that they could not easily attain by land attack. Once in these positions they have definite tasks to perform, tasks of a specialized, highly trained infantry. Getting into position by parachute is neither difficult nor hazardous. But the real work these men must do starts once they are on the ground. In all the training of parachutists so far, there has been only one fatal accident: a chute failed to open during a very low jump. During the same period of time four other parachutists were killed. These men were victims of a device far more deadly than the parachute —they were killed in auto accidents.

American paratroops are fully equipped for their task. Even their clothing is specially designed to make their work easier. The men wear heavy olive-drab jump suits. The material is snag-proof, and does not tear easily. This one-piece suit is fitted with zippers. The men get in and out of it easily. In their pockets the paratroopers carry first-aid equipment, ammunition, hand grenades, emergency rations, and wire-

A SKI-PARATROOPER LANDING IN THE SNOW. THE MASK
PROTECTS HIS FACE FROM THE BITING WIND

cutting tools. With this protective suit go special
boots. The soles are lined with sponge rubber to ab-
sorb the shock of landing. The uppers are reinforced
to prevent sprained ankles. The men wear padded
helmets with chin protectors.

SKI-PARATROOPERS IN ACTION. GUNS, AMMUNITION, AND
SKIS ARE DROPPED IN SPECIAL SUPPLY CHUTES

Our parachute troops, like those of European
armies, need fighting equipment for use the moment
they land. The men carry sidearms and, under war
conditions, would carry grenades in their jump suit
pockets. Supply parachutes of different colors

dropped from the transport planes bring automatic rifles and machine guns. Even heavier weapons have been dropped by parachutes: 37 and 50 millimeter machine guns and anti-tank guns; 60 millimeter trench mortars and 75 millimeter howitzers. Besides actual fighting equipment the paratroops must have radio sets for communication with their base, aircraft signals, and rockets. Additional food rations and first-aid equipment may be dropped with the troops. Dynamite may also be dropped, if the paratroops are expected to destroy bridges, railroads, or other communications.

The different-colored parachutes enable the force to identify those bearing guns, ammunition, or food. To confuse the enemy, the color of the supply chutes is constantly changed. One day a red chute may carry ammunition, another day a machine gun, and on a third day red will indicate first-aid equipment. The supplies are packed securely to prevent breakage when they land, but each container opens quickly to save time.

A new paratroop organization was formed in the winter of 1941 as the first unit of the 504th Parachute Battalion. By early spring of 1942 the men were on active maneuvers. This new group is our ski-paratroops—a unit composed of trained jumpers who are also experts on skis. These men have learned to jump and land in high mountain snows. Their skis and fighting equipment are dropped beside them. Within a few minutes after they have landed, these white-clad troops, fully armed, ski toward their objective. Their warm water-proof garments blend with the snow and make the men practically invisible. Ski troops, landing high on the snowy slopes, can take and hold a mountain pass, disrupt communication, and hinder the enemy in many ways.

How fast we are now training paratroops and how many thousands of chutists we have are, of course, military secrets, too valuable to the enemy to be reported at this time. But if Ben Franklin could see our battalions of trained paratroops today, he would be proud of them. His dream of "ten thousand men descending from the clouds" may soon come true.

Chapter Twelve

PARATROOP TRAINING

IN the United States Army each paratrooper is considered an expert. The rating of "parachutist" is the equivalent of a Specialist First Class. As specialists, parachutists receive $50 a month extra "jumping pay." They are the highest paid army unit outside the air corps. This extra pay attracts some of the volunteers to the parachute battalions. Others join because they know how important the work of the paratroops is and want to do their share. Still others come in search of excitement and adventure.

Every parachutist becomes an expert the hard way.

154

Weeks of intensive schooling, practice, and experience slowly turn the recruit into a trained jumper. This training began even before the volunteer was accepted by the parachute school. Each applicant must have at least six months of training in the regular infantry camps, or have had previous army experience. His military progress, his ability, and his character are, therefore, on record. These records were carefully considered with each application. The strict requirements for parachutists and the careful selection of the best of the applicants make certain that the men who finally reach Fort Benning are the cream of the army.

Each new contingent of parachutists coming to the Georgia school brings together a crowd of athletes of which any college might be proud. As soon as these newcomers reach Fort Benning their training begins. First they study the parachute: its parts, construction, forms, and uses. Each man learns to know every detail. He has at his finger tips more facts than even you will have when you have finished this book. He not only learns about the parachute, but he becomes thoroughly familiar with the chute itself. He knows how it feels, how to fold it; how to shake out the silk shroud lines; how to carry and store it. He learns how to pack his own chute methodically and carefully. Each fold must fit exactly; each cord must be in its proper place. No student parachutist will risk a careless mistake when he knows that soon he will be jumping with the chute he has packed himself. It may take the student two hours or more to pack his chute. Time is not important at first. The job must be done perfectly. Speed comes with longer experience.

Beside this ground work with parachutes, the volunteers continue their training with a variety of weapons: grenades, automatic rifles, and machine guns. They learn how to handle dynamite and other explosives, how to use wire-cutting tools. They practice surprise maneuvers. Team work is essential for the success of paratroops. The men are taught to work together, each doing his specific job accurately and promptly.

A strenuous program of physical education goes on at the same time. To see these paratroops in training might lead you to think that you have come across a group of circus acrobats in rehearsal. The men learn to roll, tumble, and somersault, so they can land on their feet from any position. They learn to climb ropes and jump from platforms. They develop their chest muscles, shoulders, arms and legs. Each chutist is trained on the "death ride." Here he gets the same experience as he would in dropping with a chute. Each man learns to roll forward on landing and to get to his feet without being dragged along by the wind-blown chute. He discovers how to spill the air quickly from his chute, so that danger from the ground winds is eliminated.

The men practice jumping from five- and eight-foot platforms. Landing from these heights is the equivalent of coming down in a chute. They leap from the door of a dummy plane and discover how important it is for them to respond quickly to the signal and jump clear without hesitation. For weeks this training goes on, until the volunteer has done everything except actually jump.

Jumping begins at the 250-foot towers. These huge skeletons of steel work impress the volunteer from the first day he arrives. Crowning the tower are four steel arms stretching out like compass points. Cables connect from these arms to the ground. Inside the steel frame is the engine room where the spinning drums pull the hoisting cables up and down.

At the control tower the trainee gets five rides on a parachute chair exactly like that used by over a million visitors at the New York World's Fair. Eight guide cables control the chute and shock absorbers limit the jolt on landing. The first drop is a thrill. The second is exciting. The thrill wears off and the student gains confidence. The third, fourth, and fifth drops are so unexciting that the student has a chance to look around, watch the parachute, and learn what is going on. After he has passed this beginning stage, the student makes several more parachute descents in the controlled parachute. This time he wears a regulation parachute harness instead of sitting on a swing. Now there are no shock absorbers to ease his landing, though the first few times there may be a rubber cushion under his feet. If he has learned his lessons well, he will land relaxed and safe with his knees bent. If not, the officer in charge will correct his mistakes at once and the student gets a chance to

ON THE 250-FOOT TOWERS AT FORT BENNING THE PARA-
TROOPERS GET THEIR FIRST PRACTICAL EXPERIENCE WITH
CHUTES

try again and again.

The next phase of training takes place at the free tower. This tower is so arranged that the parachutes are hoisted up, attached to a large ring. When they are released the parachute floats free with no cable to guide it. At first a 32-foot parachute is used, providing a slower descent. Later the standard 28-foot parachute is substituted. The trainee takes his place under the ring hoist. His parachute is connected and at the signal the cable hauls him up. The apparatus stops near the top, allowing time for any oscillations to disappear. Then the chute is released. It floats downward, sometimes carried off to one side by the wind. The student steers the chute by pulling the shroud lines. He learns to twist in his harness, so he will land facing the wind. As soon as he spills the air from the chute, he is ready to start again.

From the moment training began, officers have carefully watched each volunteer. During all the ground training a weeding-out process has been going on. Of the volunteers about 15% are returned to their outfits before they have made their first plane jump. At each step in the training a few fall by the

Official Photograph, U. S. Army Air Corp

PARATROOPERS AT THEIR FIRST JUMP. THE STATIC LINE, HOOKED TO THE WIRE, PULLS THE PACK OPEN WHEN THE · JUMPER IS CLEAR OF THE PLANE

wayside. Some are not tough enough to stand the strenuous program. Some are temperamentally un-suited. Occasionally the tower jumps prove too much for a husky six-footer. He just can't take it and is quietly transferred back to the ground troops. Weeding out continues during the practice jumps. A man who is too tense or nervous will not make a good parachutist. Men sometimes lose their courage when they see the open door of the plane and the void below. No force or persuasion is used. The trainee who fails is quietly transferred from the school before the day is out.

By now the men are eager for their first real jump from a plane. Six weeks of training have already gone by. They feel like veterans and look forward to real experience. For their first jump the trainees go up in a large transport plane—twelve men, a lieutenant, and a non-com. An extra parachute attached to a dummy is taken along. Oscar, the dummy, has the privilege of being the first to jump. His fall shows the direction and speed of the wind.

The men sit in two rows, facing each other. Some are apprehensive, others joke and wisecrack. Above their heads along the center of the plane runs a steel wire. For these practice jumps each man wears two parachutes. Attached to each man's main chute is a folded rope with a snap hook at the end. This static

THESE MEN ARE GOING UP FOR ANOTHER JUMP. ABOUT
20 MEN JUMP FROM EACH PLANE

line will pull the chute from the pack as soon as the
chutist has jumped.

The second chute each man wears is in a front pack.
This chute has a 24-foot canopy and falls slightly
faster than the standard chutes. Should the static

line fail to open the main chute, the emergency chute may be used. As the jumper leaps clear of the plane, he counts slowly: "1001, 1002, 1003, 1004." Four seconds have gone by. A parachute will normally open in less than two. If by now the jumper hasn't felt the tug of the tightening harness, it's time for him to pull the emergency rip cord. Stop Start notes

You may wonder why the automatic type chute with static line, that was considered unsatisfactory in 1919, is now used by our paratroops. There are two answers. First, these are not 1919 type chutes; they are the latest and best, a great deal better than World War I types. Second, the men are jumping from a cabin of a transport plane under conditions entirely different from the open cockpit of a 1918 type biplane. The overhead static line, the large door, the perfected chute, all make the paratrooper's jump just as safe as the man's who pulls his own rip cord. The present arrangement permits better control and co-ordination of the jumping party, without increased hazard.

The big plane levels off at 1,500 feet and slows down to about 90 miles an hour. The time has come.

THESE SKI-PARATROOPERS HAVE OBTAINED THEIR SKIS AND GUNS FROM SUPPLY CHUTES
AND ARE NOW READY TO GO

Parachutes

The jump master commands "Stand up!" The men form a single line, facing the door at the rear of the plane. They adjust their helmets and hitch their parachutes so the harness fits easier. At the command "Hook up," each catches the hook of his 15-foot static line to the overhead cable. At this stage of the training the officer jumps first. He takes his place in the door, feet spread apart. He shouts "Go," and jumps clear of the plane. The novices follow him one after another, less than a second apart. If they keep the tradition of Fort Benning each will yell "Geronimo" as he bails out on his initial jump.

The custom of yelling the name of this famous Indian chief started with a member of one of the first groups training at Fort Benning. The night before his first jump, the trainee had been to see a movie about this daring Indian. As the jumper leaped the first time next day he shouted "Geronimo," and every chutist has done it since.

In one minute or less after the jump master has gone over the side, his dozen students are floating in the air with him. Each knows exactly what to do in steering his chute and controlling oscillations. In another minute, all have landed. They quickly regain their feet, spill the air from their chutes, and gather together to get praise and criticism. Chutes are re-packed, other jumps scheduled.

Each man must make five jumps: three solos and two mass jumps before he is qualified to receive his parachutist insignia. When these requirements have been met, the candidate graduates. He is now per-mitted to sew on his uniform the silver parachute with wings extended at each side—the emblem of the paratroops. It is an emblem each volunteer has earned through hard work, and an emblem he is proud of.

But training continues even for the full-fledged parachutist. Some may assist with the new recruits. Others learn to do special tasks, such as demolition work or signaling. All take part in maneuvers. They practice attacks on enemy airfields. They learn how to strike quickly and effectively in the shortest pos-sible time. All this training continues with but a sin-gle purpose: When the hour for action comes, we can count on the army and its parachute battalions.

Chapter Thirteen

THE REST OF THE FIGHTING FORCE

ARMIES of paratroops are something new. They have proved their military worth and the idea is spreading. The marines have always had the reputation for doing a thorough job. Whatever the trouble, the marines have been quick to reach the danger spot. Now, with parachutes, they can get there even faster. The marine paratroops are in many ways similar to those of the army. The group is naturally smaller, but they can do everything the army can and insist they can do it better.

Marine paratroopers are broken in by two weeks of intensive training with their own unit before being

A NAVY PILOT READY TO BAIL OUT. ALL BRANCHES OF THE
ARMED FORCES USE PARACHUTES

transferred to the parachute battalion for advanced instruction. Their training is rigorous. As with the army, only young, tough athletes are accepted for this work. The marine units have been training in New Jersey, Virginia, and at a Pacific coast base, where a new 250-foot training tower is under construction.

The marines had two companies in their parachute battalion at the start. A second battalion has been formed and the corps is hoping to turn out 300 trained paratroops a month. The first group graduated at Lakehurst in the fall of 1941. Fifty-six men completed their training and did their "graduating" jumps. They received their parachutist's insignia and now many are helping to train the new volunteers.

Dramatic as the paratroops are, we cannot forget that the armed forces were using chutes long before paratroops were dreamed of. Both the army and navy air corps have continually used chutes. Every man entering a military plane must wear one. These chutes are intended for the good old-fashioned purpose of saving the lives of aviators in an emergency. This makes their use very different from that of paratroops. The air corps and the pilots would be just as happy if they never used their chutes. The less they are used, the better it is. Fewer forced jumps mean that pilots are careful, their machines are good—and if there has been a fight, that they are better than the enemy. Paratroops are trained to use their chutes; pilots are so trained they won't have to.

At Randolph Field, the "West Point of the Air," pilots in training fly a total of 150,000 miles each day, practicing navigation, landing, and maneuvering. Their skill can be measured by the number of emergency forced jumps. Of the 1,000 parachutes in constant use only 37 have been opened in emergency jumps. These 37 emergency jumps have spread over an 11-year period. Some have been from dual control planes, so that the actual number of emergencies is even less than 37.

But accidents may happen, and even the best of pilots may have to bail out some time. What training does the pilot or the gunner have in preparation for such an emergency? The answer is—just enough. Both the army and navy air corps take the attitude that an aviator using his chute must use it right the first time.

All he has to do is jump, count, and pull the rip cord. If his parachute fails, the pilot who jumps never has a chance to profit by his mistake. Practice jumps and extensive training would not be worth the effort. Once an aviator knows how a chute works and how to use it, he is well prepared.

Early in their training at any of the major airfields the embryo pilots are given chute instruction. They have an opportunity to see the chutes, study their parts, try the harness, and learn how to use them. They learn the best way to leave a crippled plane; what to do if the plane is spinning, and other practical things. All their training is on the ground. Once they know how to use the chute, they need no further lessons.

The importance of this training can only be appreciated when the total number of pilots, gunners, and navigators in service is known. Our air force is increasing at a tremendous rate. This year, 50,000 planes will come off the assembly lines, and double that number the year following. This mixture of fighters and bombers will require an average of three men to man each plane. On this basis the next two years will

Official Photograph U. S. Navy

AVIATION CADETS RECEIVING GROUND TRAINING IN THE
USE OF PARACHUTES

see nearly half a million men in aviation. Each will know how to use a parachute.

Neither army nor navy pilots maintain their own chutes. A chute is assigned to a pilot. He has the harness fitted. He wears the chute every time he is aloft and stores it in his locker when his air duty is over. Every sixty days he turns in his chute to the licensed parachute riggers attached to each airfield. These men inspect the chute, make any repairs, and carefully repack. Parachute riggers are experts in their work. At Randolph Field, Texas, over a thousand chutes are inspected, repaired, and repacked every 60-day period.

Parachute riggers are carefully trained. They must have experience and pass written and practical tests before they are licensed. The parachute loft, where the riggers work, is often a corner of the hangars or some similar place with a high roof. There must be plenty of room to hoist the unfolded chutes and dry them properly. Often the room is heated to aid the drying. The riggers also require long smooth tables, at least 3 feet wide and 40 feet long. On these the chutes are stretched. First the canopies are shaken

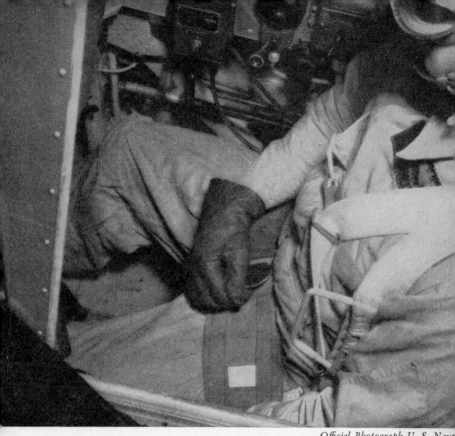

Official Photograph U. S. Navy

IN AN EMERGENCY THE PILOT RELEASES HIS SAFETY BELT
AND BAILS OUT. HE COUNTS FOUR TO CLEAR THE PLANE
AND THEN PULLS THE RIP CORD, SEEN CLEARLY ON HIS
LEFT SIDE

free of wrinkles and are folded smooth, one section
at a time, then the shroud lines are stowed away, and
the folded chute is carefully packed.

You never hear much about the riggers who keep

at their job day after day at army and navy fields. They can't take chances; their job must be 100% perfect. In nine years the two expert riggers at Randolph Field have drop-tested over 7,000 chutes that they have packed. Every single one opened promptly. That is why army and navy pilots have no doubts about their chutes. They know the riggers have done their job well—so well that everyone takes a perfect job for granted. Parachute riggers don't get medals for their work. Maybe they should.

The army and navy air corps use other chutes besides those worn by the pilots. Parachute flares are carried on board most planes and are often used. A plane coming into a small airport or making an emergency landing may drop a parachute flare to light the way in. There are several types of these flares. Generally they burn from one to three minutes. The flare contains magnesium that burns with an intense white light illuminating wide areas. Large flares reach nearly a million candle power and are sufficient to illuminate an area over a mile square. The flares are equipped with a delayed action mechanism that does not light the magnesium till the flare has fallen clear of the

THE MARINE PARATROOPS ARE A SMALL BUT WELL-
TRAINED UNIT. HERE ARE SOME MEMBERS GOING UP FOR
A PRACTICE JUMP

ship. The parachute delays the fall so the pilot can
make the most use of the light.

The "Meteor" and "Schmittner" flares used in Germany recently are good examples of parachute il-
lumination. The flares are packed in a metal container
attached to the shroud lines by a chain. This elimi-

nates danger from fire. The entire apparatus weighs about 75 pounds. The flare is not ignited until the chute opens. This can be arranged by a clockwork mechanism that releases the canopy when the chute has fallen the desired distance—usually between 150 and 5,000 feet below the plane. The flares are of several types, producing from 150,000 to 500,000 candle power and burning as long as four minutes.

Besides the flares that burn as the parachute descends, planes may drop "light bombs" by chute. These ignite only when they hit the ground. A percussion cap sets the mixture off. One type gives 80,000 candle power and burns for 100 seconds. In this time the pilot may be able to make a safe emergency landing.

In wartime the use of parachute flares is increased. Planes on a night raid will drop parachute flares to illuminate their target before dropping a stick of bombs. Photographs taken before and after, often with the help of these same flares, will make it possible to plan new attacks and estimate the damage done.

The Rest of the Fighting Force

There are many types of military flares. Besides those of long and short duration, there are signal flares burning different colors or combinations of colors. Parachute flares are so arranged that the flare canister is interchangeable, permitting the pilot to attach the correct signal to the chute at a moment's notice. These flares are a quick means of sending orders at night to scattered units. Not only are signal flares dropped from planes but they may be shot from special guns or sent up as rockets. In either case the charge explodes high in the air. A small parachute to which the flare is attached is released and floats slowly to earth as the signal burns.

We have a new type of parachute flare that does not burn steadily. After it has fallen it gives out a powerful flash of light like some superflashlight bulb. The camera in the observing plane is synchronized with the parachute flash by means of an electric eye. With this type of flare, the airman gets his picture. The flash is so quick and so bright it does not reveal the plane to anti-aircraft batteries below.

Besides flares, there are distinct parachute weapons. The R.A.F. Bomber Command for nearly two years has mined enemy waters with parachute mines. Another weapon, the parachute bomb, is also being perfected. This bomb is designed to make one of the faster American bombers even more effective.

The Douglas light bomber, the A-20A, has proved itself one of the best. It is an attack bomber (A stands for attack) with a top speed of 380 miles an hour. It is easily maneuvered and is an ideal ship for low contour flying or, as the pilots say, grass cutting. Because it can race along at terrific speed 75 or 100 feet above the ground, the A-20A can be the terror of communication lines, roads, and railroads. It can come in over the tree tops and its speed makes it relatively safe from machine gun fire.

But flying so low, the A-20A is likely to be a victim of its own bombs. Bombs dropped from only 75 feet would practically explode underneath the plane. They would certainly destroy the enemy's trucks but might also throw the bomber out of control. This would be serious at low altitude. A parachute bomb seems to be the answer. These bombs will be dropped automatically at intervals as the plane swoops low over a transport column. The small parachutes will retard their fall just a few seconds, enough time for the plane to get out of danger, but not enough to let the enemy escape. This weapon has not yet been tested in battle.

Chapter Fourteen

WORLD WAR II

IF some future historian should call the Second World War "The War from the Air," his label would be substantially correct. Air power has come to its own during this war, and air-borne troops have played an increasingly important part in operations. From the very beginning, parachute troops have been in action. Russia first used them in the Russo-Finnish phase of the war in 1939. White-clad Russian fighters dropped behind the Finnish lines. The complete story is still in the hands of the censors. The Finns claimed that the paratroops were completely wiped out. The Russians claimed success. The truth may lie somewhere between the two claims. At any rate, paratroops had their first test in battle. The fact that they have been used over and over again by both the Axis and the United Nations since those first days shows that paratroops have value.

A parachute training program had started in Russia in 1930. By 1933 it was nationwide. Goering is reported to have organized the first German parachute battalions in 1933. Men as young as 17 years were selected and put through a course of rigorous training that included ground practice, jumping, falling, rolling, and all sorts of military team work. The German paratroopers practiced low jumps—as dangerously low as 400 feet.

After the Germans overran Poland, it is reported that they drove every inhabitant from several towns and villages. The areas around these towns were closed and carefully guarded. Here during the winter of 1939 and early spring of 1940 the German parachute troops engaged in continual practice. The troops learned to jump from bombers and reassemble quickly on the ground. They learned how to land on roofs and to start fires to distract the inhabitants. They learned how to disrupt communication and transportation, and how to seize and hold strategic points.

These were the trained parachute troops Germany used in her attacks on the Low Countries in May, 1940. Rotterdam, The Hague, Delft, Leiden, and a number of other centers were attacked simultaneously. The Dutch were taken completely by surprise. The story of the attack on the Rotterdam airport is typical and shows clearly how parachute troops are used.

Early on the morning of May 10th, when the airport was still half hidden by the morning fog, German bombers flew in at low altitude, probably not more than 300 feet from the ground. As they neared the airport, the paratroops jumped one after another through the cabin door. About twenty men came from each plane. Within a minute the entire attacking force had landed. Each man had a definite task. One group cut telephone wires. Others silenced the anti-aircraft batteries. The bombers circled and returned, bombing the hangars and adding to the panic. Ten minutes later the airport was surrounded.

The first wave of the attack was followed by trans-

Sovfo

PARACHUTING IN RUSSIAN ARMY MANEUVERS. RUSSIA HAS
LED THE WORLD IN PARACHUTING

port planes bringing troops. Eight hundred men were
quickly landed with complete light equipment. These
squads set up machine gun nests, occupied buildings
and strategic points. One hour after the attack started
the entire airport was in German hands. This force
held the airport alone without reinforcements for
three days. Then the first motorized infantry arrived
to relieve the paratroopers and air-borne troops.

At all other places the Germans used similar meth-

ods. At Liége, planes first dropped a smoke screen to
protect the landing force. But the same pattern was
used: sudden attack, capture, and holding out till
land forces arrived. The first phases of the war from
the air were definitely in favor of the attacker.

It is not the intention here to write a history of
this war, but a brief account of how parachutes have
changed modern warfare. We can, therefore, skip an
entire year, during which time the scene of action
shifted from Western Europe to the Mediterranean.
By May, 1941, Greece had been overrun and the
British were still attempting to hold Crete. In the
battle for Crete, parachute troops were used on a
larger scale than ever before.

On May 16th the Germans began a continued air
attack. Planes were constantly over the island, pound-
ing at the British airports. Within the next few days
the few R.A.F. planes that represented British air
power were practically destroyed. The Germans controlled the air. Early on the morning of the 20th the
air attack was renewed with even greater vigor; wave
after wave of planes came over the island. Fighter
planes zoomed low over the hills, machine-gunning
the British trenches. Bombers attacked camps and all

points of occupation. Every sort of aerial weapon was used, but the British hugged their trenches and escaped with few casualties.

Then an eyewitness reported a distinct lull. The defending troops had barely relaxed when a huge formation of Junker transports passed overhead and paratroops started dropping from the skies. With the troops came parachutes bearing ammunition, machine guns, and supplies. Many of these soldiers were killed before they reached ground. Parties landed all over the island—about 3,000 troops in all. Some managed to take defensive positions which they held till reinforcements came.

The next day the parachute attacks continued. These, and the continual bombardment from the air, gave the Germans the opportunity to get a foothold. As soon as the airports were captured, transport planes brought in thousands of troops as rapidly as the planes could land and take off. Troops and supplies came in on gliders too. Under pressure of air attacks and increasing enemy ground fire, the British made a gradual retreat to the south side of the island where they were successfully evacuated.

The successful use of parachute troops was not all

on the Axis side. In February the British dropped a small picked parachute unit near Mt. Vulture in southern Italy. This task force volunteered to destroy reservoirs and communications. No follow-up was planned. Once they landed, the men were on their own. How well they succeeded no one will know till the war is over. The British were satisfied. Their office of information points out that the Italians refused to let neutral observers visit the area for a long time after the paratroops had made this raid.

As the war spread, the use of parachute troops did also. Japan used a mass parachute attack against Java early in 1942. In one day the Dutch reported 700 paratroopers killed. Again details are unobtainable, but the Japanese using the German blitz technique did take Java.

March, 1942, brought more news of troops from the skies. As the month opened the British made a night surprise attack on a radio base in occupied France. Commandos landed from barges and parachutists in dark clothes and black chutes dropped from the skies. The surprise attack was a complete success. The station was destroyed and the attackers

THESE U. S. PARATROOPERS ARE READY FOR ACTION
WITHIN 10 SECONDS AFTER THEY LAND

were picked up safely by naval units. Later in the month came news of another surprise attack on the submarine base at St. Nazaire. Again parachute troops assisted in the successful hit and run raid.

Parachute troops were used by the British in their successful occupation of the island of Madagascar in May, 1942. The paratroopers and the planes from which they dropped were brought to the vicinity of the island on aircraft carriers. Simultaneous parachute, plane, and naval attack brought the island under British control in short order.

Each major army in the war is training paratroops. Every weak spot is in potential danger from sky invaders. Our own paratroops are steadily increasing in number. If we are to go by the thoroughness of their training, they will give a good account of themselves when the time comes.

Chutes were not only used by land troops in World War II but at sea as well. Even before the war started, Hitler boasted of a secret weapon his armies would use. By October, 1939, it became clear that this secret weapon was a new type of mine—a magnetic mine. The principal difference in the new type of mine is the way it explodes. Usually a ship must strike a mine to set it off. A magnetic mine will explode if a ship merely passes near by—no actual contact is necessary. Inside the mine is a balanced magnetic needle. The iron hull of a passing ship will attract this needle and cause it to turn, following the ship. When the needle has turned sufficiently it touches a contact point, completing an electric circuit. This current explodes the mine.

Magnetic mines are dangerous. Their danger increases greatly if they can be dropped in harbors or bays where ships must pass. That is exactly what Germany attempted to do. In the early days of the war, bombers flew into channel ports and up the Thames, dropping magnetic mines by parachute.

The technique of parachuting mines requires skill. If the mines are dropped from too great a height, the parachutes will drift and the mines will not land in the ship channels. There must be just enough time for the chute to operate. Allowance must be made for wind and drift.

The British were quick to follow a good example. Less than six months after the first magnetic mines

J. S. Army Signal Corps Photo

AUTOMATIC RIFLES, MACHINE GUNS, MORTARS, AND
SMALL CANNON HAVE BEEN DROPPED BY PARACHUTE TO
PARATROOPERS. HERE WEAPONS ARE BEING PACKED

were dropped in their waters, the British were ready
to return the favor. Magnetic mines were being man-
ufactured and two-motored Hampton bombers were
transformed into mine-layers.

The British chose seven areas to be mined. These included French and Dutch coastal points, Norwegian waters, the Kiel Canal, and several others. They set to work with care. Bombers accurately patrolled the area, often flying up and down several times before the altitude and wind were right for releasing the parachute mines. With accurate navigation and close observance of landmarks it was possible to land the mines exactly where they would do the most damage. This was often done in the face of enemy fighter action.

Within a few seconds after he drops a bomb, the bomber knows his results. With a mine, only time can tell. A mine may lie in the water for weeks or months before it takes effect. However, the British have slowly gathered records that show their parachute mines have been effective. For a while part of the Kiel Canal was closed. Six ships were sunk and six damaged in Norwegian waters, seventeen sunk off Denmark, and others off the coasts of France and Belgium. When the war is over and the last record is written, we shall know exactly how successful parachutes have been at sea.

Chapter Fifteen

SMOKE JUMPING

THE parachute has often been called the "Life Saver of the Air." This title is well deserved. Since 1939 parachutes have been used in a brand-new type of life saving, that of saving our forests from their worst enemy—fire. About fifteen million acres of forest, it has been estimated, cannot be easily reached by roads or trails. Fires starting in these areas (mostly in the Northwest) have the opportunity to get a good start before fire fighters can penetrate the wilderness. Time is an important factor in fire fighting. A small fire—which could be easily put out—is far more difficult and costly to control once it has made headway.

The U. S. Forest Service, as early as 1934, started to experiment with the idea of dropping men and supplies by parachute near the scene of forest fires. These early experiments near Ogden, Utah, were quite successful. Drops with dummies and live drops were made. Yet the idea failed to take root and was not put into practice until five years later.

In the summer of 1939 the Forest Service inaugurated a whole series of experiments, using airplanes to fight forest fires. The training of the first crew of parachute fire fighters was part of this undertaking. That year enough jumps were made to show that the idea was sound and that jumps could be made safely in all kinds of forest country. At first professional parachutists were used. But very soon volunteer foresters, who had never seen a chute before, were trained for this work. These men tried jumping over ground that varied in elevation from sea level to over 8,000 feet. They practiced landing in sixteen different types of forest terrain. By the end of the summer the methods of jumping forest fires were well established. The other rangers promptly took these para-

chutists to heart and soon named them "smoke jumpers."

In 1940 the experiment was extended to two forest
regions. News of it spread through the Forest Service.
There were about one hundred applicants for the
eight positions on the first parachute squadron. The
men were required to be between the ages of 21 and
35. Their weight had to be less than 190 pounds. Each
had to pass a pilot's physical examination. A crew of
seven was selected for a two-week training period
consisting of two days' ground practice followed by
jumping practices. After two weeks of training, they
became full-fledged "smoke jumpers."

The first opportunity for the smoke jumpers to
try their skill came on July 12, 1940, when a fire was
sighted twelve miles from the Ranger Station across
very rough country in the Nez Perce National Forest.
The smoke jumpers were summoned. They dropped
at the fire and set to work. The next day a crew of
four foresters came through on foot to help finish
the job. Previously for a fire of this type a crew of
twenty-five men would have been sent.

During that summer smoke jumpers were dropped

U. S. Forest Service Photo

SMOKE JUMPERS HAVE BEEN TRAINED TO LAND IN ALL
KINDS OF WOODED COUNTRY. ONCE THEY HAVE LANDED
THEIR JOB IS FIRE FIGHTING

at nine fires in this Forest Service region. It took on the average an hour and three-quarters to reach the fire by plane and chute. The average time for a ground crew of forest fighters to arrive was twenty-eight hours. Two or three smoke jumpers can control a fire and prevent it from doing any serious damage, whereas in the old days by the time a ground crew arrived many more were needed to control a much enlarged fire. On the basis of the first year's experiments the cost of putting out a fire by parachute dropped to about $250. To put out the same type of fire with a ground crew would have cost about $3,500.

Smoke jumping is a unique profession. The men, first of all, are trained foresters who know exactly what to do when they land. They are able to care for themselves in the wilderness, do their own cooking, swing an ax or a shovel, pack their heavy equipment to the spot where it is needed. These men are ready to start fighting a fire within a few minutes after they land.

Smoke jumpers in working clothes really look like men from Mars. They wear special clothing to protect them when they land. Jumping suits are made of heavy canvas, zippered for immediate disrobing. The suits are well padded. Smoke jumpers wear an exaggerated football helmet with a heavy wire mask. Ankle braces are worn over ordinary boots to prevent spraining ankles. Thus protected, landing on a tree-top is as safe, if not safer, than landing on the ground. In the pocket of his uniform the ranger carries a strong rope to lower himself from trees.

Smoke jumpers use a special 30-foot parachute carried in a back pack. This chute is built with special features to eliminate oscillation. It is easily controlled by guide flaps. The jumper can guide his landing to within a few hundred feet of his target. The smoke jumper also carries a 27-foot chest pack parachute for emergency use. If caught in a tree the man can quickly release himself because the harness of this chute is specially arranged.

Because of its larger size, the chute used by fire fighters has the additional advantage of descending at a speed of about 12 feet per second. This is about one-third slower than the rate of standard chutes. Because of this the jumper has more time to size up

. S. *Forest Service Photo*

SMOKE JUMPERS USE A SPECIAL CHUTE THAT DROPS
SLOWER THAN STANDARD MODELS. THE MEN CAN STUDY
THE FIRE AS THEY FALL AND STEER TOWARD THE BEST
LANDING

ground conditions and steer toward the best landing
place. In making tests with these parachutes in mountain areas, it was found that the elevation has very
little effect on landings. A jumper leaving a plane at
10,000 feet to land on an 8,000-foot mountain descends just as easily as one jumping from an altitude
of 2,000 feet above sea level.

In a pocket on the parachute pack is a miniature high frequency radio. This complete two-way set weighs only six pounds, is less than a foot long, and five inches high. It is simple and dependable. Within five minutes after landing, the ranger can be in radio contact with the plane that brought him.

When a fire is sighted in an inaccessible spot, the smoke jumpers are summoned. They are prepared for an immediate take-off in a chartered plane. Supplies and equipment are loaded with them. The plane flies across the site of the fire and a small test chute with a ten pound bag of sand is released. The pilot circles, watching this chute to get an idea of the wind-drift. As he circles the second time, making allowances for the wind, he signals the jumpers to bail out. The pilot continues around, watching the jumpers land. As he circles over the spot a third time, he releases the supply parachutes. These carry down to the rangers all the supplies they will need. Soon the jumpers signal their okay. The plane returns to the airport.

The rangers immediately set to work. To check a forest fire until the ground crew arrives requires a lot of equipment. In the fire fighting pack are axes, shovels, lamps, food supplies, first-aid kit, canteen, and other necessary articles. With this the men can work at the fire for at least two days. By that time a ground crew will have come to their assistance.

The Forest Service has done a thorough job in working out the problem of dropping supplies. This has worked so well that even the ground crews receive their supplies by parachute as well as the smoke jumpers. Hundreds of tons of food and equipment have been dropped in this way. Cases of eggs, axes, first-aid supplies, radio sets, are among those that have been landed safely by parachute.

For landing supplies two kinds of parachutes have been developed. One is a 9-by-9-foot parachute. The other is 10 by 10 feet. Both of these are made from ten or twelve ounce burlap with linen shroud lines. The cost of the parachutes is about $1.25 each. The Forest Service has worked out a standard procedure for making these chutes, folding, and using them. Tests have shown that these burlap parachutes will support a weight of about one pound for each square foot of canopy during descent. When so loaded the parachute descends at a rate of 40 feet per second. At

ALL SUPPLIES FOR THE SMOKE JUMPERS ARE DROPPED BY
SUPPLY CHUTES. THE YELLOW STREAMER MAKES THE
CHUTE EASIER TO LOCATE

this rate very little damage is done when the load is landed. A long yellow streamer attached to the canopy enables the men on the ground to spot it and to recover the load.

Special packing is required for some of these supplies. For example, a crate of eggs to be dropped by parachute is first cut in half and the open ends are sealed. The half crate is packed with excelsior in a burlap sack and lowered by a 9-by-9-foot parachute. Such items as axes, lanterns, fresh fruit, saws, telephones, water, and gasoline require special packing, but all can be safely dropped. At one fire in California over ten thousand pounds of food and supplies were chuted to the fire fighting crews. By means of parachutes 1,500 pounds of supplies were delivered in two hours. Pack mules would have taken 6½ hours to deliver 300 pounds.

Though smoke jumping is still in its infancy, plans for at least five squads of eight jumpers each have been developed. The records of the Forest Service show that this is a safe, cheap, and effective way of controlling certain forest fires, especially those caused by lightning in out-of-the-way places. There is every chance that the parachute corps will remain a permanent and important part of the Forest Service of the West.

Chapter Sixteen

PARACHUTES AND EXPLORATION

THE business of exploring has changed greatly since the days of Lewis and Clark. Modern expeditions use all the latest equipment. They take along radios, gasoline engines, canned foods, and airplanes. The latest aid for explorers is the parachute.

The Soviet government has used planes and chutes to drop mail and supplies to its far north outposts in Siberia and on the Arctic islands. Our own Forest Service, as you know, has used similar methods of getting supplies to fire fighting crews. In this work the parachute has been a grand success.

Parachutes and Exploration

In the midst of the Grand Canyon, cut off from both sides by the erosion of the Colorado River, is a tall butte or flat-topped mountain known as Shiva's Temple. At one time this must have been connected to the upland rim of the canyon. It has been separated for so long that any animals living on it have been living in isolation for many generations. Here was an excellent place to study the effects of environment on the evolution of animals. Scientists planned an expedition to the top of Shiva's Temple to see what they could find. With skilled packers and mountain climbers to help, they succeeded in scaling the steep walls and established a camp on the bare surface of the butte. There they set to work.

The scientists needed supplies, equipment, and especially water, as there were no springs or brooks on this arid plateau. With the help of a local pilot, some parachutes, and containers, a regular supply service was established. The party received its water supply from the Grand Canyon airport instead of having to haul it miles by mule and on foot. This help made it possible for the expedition to spend more time at collecting and study. Small mammals were caught, plant life studied, and records made. The trip was a success and the party returned safely.

When the Archbold Expedition penetrated deep into New Guinea in 1938, supplies were dropped to their base camps by parachute. More recently, Bradford Washbourne has used a similar technique in Alaska.

Walter A. Wood, head of the Department of Exploration and Field Research, American Geographical Society, had led exploring parties into the mountain wilderness of Yukon Territory since 1935. These expeditions explored many of the glaciers and peaks of the St. Elias Range on the Alaska-Canada border. The early expeditions used horses to carry their supplies. When the country became too rough, the men had to pack their own provisions and equipment. Tramping over ice fields and through snow with fifty or more pounds of equipment was not the fastest way to travel. The fact that the party traveled slowly meant that it had to carry more food and supplies. In turn, this called for a larger party and greater expense.

Another complicating factor in exploring the

THE WOOD-YUKON EXPEDITION PARACHUTED SUPPLIES TO
THEIR BASE AND TO ADVANCED SITES. THESE SUPPLIES EN-
ABLED THE PARTY TO PROCEED FASTER TOWARD THEIR
GOAL

North is the very short summer season. Unless one
can take advantage of every clear day, the season may
be over before the objective of the expedition can be
reached. To indicate the difficulty of traveling in
this region, here are some actual examples. In 1935
it required nine working days to move men and supplies a distance of twelve miles from a base camp.

These nine working days were sandwiched in between sixteen stormy days that hampered or prevented movement. In 1939 sixteen working days were required to establish advance camps on Mount Wood, though the total ground distance was only eleven miles.

Because of these difficulties any method that speeds up the delivery of supplies and equipment to advance bases is a tremendous aid to explorers. Delays in getting supplies or in moving them forward may mean the failure of an entire summer's work.

The idea of using chutes to deliver supplies was first tried in the North during the summer of 1936. Only one small plane was available and four chutes. The plane made several trips and dropped six loads of supplies at the Wood base camp. These experimental loads weighed only fifty or sixty pounds, barely enough to open the chutes. Delivery was successful and more plans were made.

The following year Walter A. Wood was with the Shiva Temple Expedition. So far the chutes had dropped supplies to men waiting on the ground below. Would it be possible to drop supplies ahead, in unexplored territory, to await the ground party's arrival? In 1941 this idea was put to test.

The Wood-Yukon Expedition of 1941 with the co-operation of the United States Army conducted a large scale experiment in parachuting supplies to a base camp and to several advanced points. According to a report of the expedition in the *Geographical Review* of January, 1942, the results were highly successful. The U. S. Army sent an official observer, two bombers and their crews. The army also supplied a number of standard parachutes. These were chutes that had been retired from active army service and were marked "Unfit for Human Use."

At the base camp seventeen parachute loads of supplies were dropped by the bombers, as well as twenty-five bundles of non-breakable equipment. Only four of the landings were unsuccessful. Three of the parachutes ripped during their descent. This was not entirely unexpected, since the chutes had been condemned and had not been recently tested. The fourth parachute landed in a glacial stream and was carried away. Even with these losses, it was estimated that less than 6% of the supplies had been de-

A DYNAMITE CAP SEVERED THE PARACHUTE FROM THE
SUPPLIES ON LANDING. THIS PREVENTED THE CHUTE
FROM DRAGGING THE BOX OVER THE GROUND

stroyed. Two thousand one hundred pounds of supplies were parachuted safely, including a case of 360
eggs (three broke).

One hundred and eighty pounds of supplies for
the advance posts were packed in each wooden crate.
This weight equals a parachute's normal load. These
boxes were so arranged that the parachutes were auto-

matically freed after landing, to prevent the boxes from being dragged over the ground by the chutes. Another problem was to locate the boxes after they had been dropped. It was expected that the boxes might have to lie anywhere from a week to two months after they were dropped, before the exploring party reached them. In the North it is quite possible for all traces of the supplies to disappear under a heavy snow even during the summer. Attached to each box were two 36-inch stakes. These were designed with a spring attachment that would swing them into an erect position after landing. A red flag attached to each stake made it easier to spot from a distance. Nine loads were parachuted to the advance campsites, distributing 1,180 pounds of food and supplies.

Aerial maps of the region were carefully studied before the two army bombers set off on their mission. Campsites were selected near conspicuous landmarks. This made it easier for the pilots to drop the parachutes on their targets and for the expedition to locate them later. To drop parachutes on designated spots in wild country crossed by deep valleys required the most skillful piloting by the bomber's crew. The planes took off one clear morning. As the landmarks came into view, the chutes were dropped. The canopies opened and the experiment had begun.

On July 15, 1941, the expedition left its base camp for an attempt to climb Mount Wood, the highest unclimbed peak in North America. The party also studied the plant life and rocks of the region. At the first campsite the load of parachuted supplies was found without any difficulty. At the second camp two parachute loads were waiting. One was almost hidden by snow and the second had nearly fallen into a large crevasse. With these supplies the party was able to make a quick attack on the peak. They succeeded in reaching the summit, even though the weather turned for the worse and the temperature fell to 2 below zero.

The next objective of the expedition was Mount Walsh—a distance twice as great from the base camp and through territory that would cut off the retreat of the party if the weather turned against them. Supplies had been parachuted to several advance campsites on the route to Mount Walsh.

SUPPLIES PARACHUTED OVER A MONTH BEFORE WERE
PRACTICALLY BURIED IN THE SNOW WHEN THE WOOD-
YUKON EXPEDITION REACHED THEM. ONLY THE TIP OF
THE 36-INCH FLAG COULD BE SEEN

At the first campsite members of the party looked
for the landmark at which the supplies were expected.
It had been agreed that the supplies were to be
dropped at a prominent pile of boulders on the
glacier. The pile was easily located on the aerial photographs in relation to neighboring peaks and val-

leys. The party looked in vain for the supplies. Both the pile of boulders and the boxes of equipment were not to be found. Finally, after an all-night search, the missing boxes were located, about a mile farther down the glacier. The pilots had agreed to drop the parachute at the pile of debris and had located this pile from aerial photographs taken in 1935. The parachuted supplies hit the target—but this was in 1941. Since 1935 the glacier had slowly moved the pile of debris about a mile down the valley. Other landmarks remained behind, but the glacier had gone on, with the pile of boulders.

At the next camp the supplies were quickly located and at the following two bases also. Skis that had been dropped with the supplies enabled the party to move faster. The expedition now crossed over into the valley where they expected to set up the last camp. Everything depended on locating the final loads. When they could first see the valley floor the men stopped and anxiously looked around for the flags. One was immediately located a few hundred yards away. The second box was harder to find. It had been completely buried in the snow and only six

U. S. Army Signal Corps Pho.

SKIS WERE FIRST PARACHUTED TO THE WOOD-YUKON EX-
PEDITION. A YEAR LATER THE ARMY PARACHUTED SKIS TO
SKI TROOPS ON MANEUVER

inches of the 36-inch stake were exposed to mark the
site. Forty-six days had gone by since the parachutes
had been dropped. The supplies were safe and in good
condition.

With these supplies the party set up a base on the

ridge of Mount Walsh. They continued their scientific work, collecting plants and rock specimens. Careful records of weather conditions were kept for study and future use. Unusually good weather favored the party. On the 17th of August they reached the summit of Mount Walsh. The expedition took observations and made its way back to the base safely. After a day's rest the group returned over the ridge and down the valley to the expedition's camp. They reached camp just two hours before a severe storm broke and a spell of bad weather set in.

The use of parachutes in exploring was an experiment. To determine its success records were kept and comparisons made. Making allowances for the nature of the country, it was estimated that even if the weather were perfect it would take a minimum of ten days to reach Mount Wood from the base camp. In 1939 the actual time taken was sixteen days and the party failed to reach the summit. In 1941, with the advance parachute camps, the distance was covered in five days. The estimated minimum time to reach Mount Walsh was computed to be eighteen days. The time taken in 1941 with four parachute camps was six days. Thus by the use of advance camps with parachuted supplies the time of exploring may be cut to one-half or one-third. There is less physical strain on individual members of the party and more time available for scientific work.

Exploration is the latest field in which parachutes have been used. Here the parachute seems invaluable. Future explorers may well follow the example of the Wood-Yukon Expedition.

Chapter Seventeen

PARACHUTES AND THE WEATHER

IFTY years ago, the weather was a topic to discuss when conversation lagged. You couldn't do much about it anyhow and one man's opinion was as good as another's. People stayed inside while it rained and stormed, waiting for the skies to clear. Nowadays things move fast and we cannot afford to wait for the weather. Time is valuable. We must pay more attention to storms, wind, and rain than we ever did before. No man can change the weather, but we can take advantage of every minute we gain by accurate forecasts.

One very important change in the past twenty-five years has increased our concern about the weather conditions. The air has now become an ocean through which we constantly travel. Air lanes have become as important as sea lanes. The years have ticked off our progress from the first passenger flights. Airmail came next, then the multi-motored planes. Scheduled air routes spread over the face of the country. New airports developed, speed records were broken, the stratoliner appeared. Each step forward made weather knowledge a bit more important.

The weather is no more than a study of the changes in this ocean of air through which planes skim at speeds up to 400 miles an hour. The swirling, mixing masses of warm and cold air that control the weather in the temperate zones must be studied carefully. These masses determine rain, wind, and storm. The path and movement of each storm must be calculated and charted in advance. Its speed and growth must be watched until it is no longer observable.

Moving masses of air may first bring cold, icy winds from the north, then warm winds from the south with fog and rain—depending on the direction in which the air masses revolve and the energy they display. Small disturbances may only unsettle the air near the surface, producing a local rain or change of wind. On a larger scale, gigantic masses of air, covering hundreds of square miles, move across the continent producing wide changes in weather that extend vertically as well as horizontally.

The rotation of the earth affects these masses of air, as does the disposition of the continents and the oceans. For these and many other reasons the air at heights of one, two, three, or five miles may display characteristics quite different from those on the surface. At an altitude of one-half mile there may be an easterly wind. One mile higher the wind may blow in exactly the opposite direction, and still higher it may once again become easterly. Rain, clouds, fog, temperature, humidity, and pressure are all affected by altitude, just as conditions in the ocean are affected by depth. As long as men stayed close to the earth, the disturbances of the upper air meant very little. But as balloons and airplanes ascended higher and higher and stratoliners streaked across the continent at altitudes close to five miles, the disturbances of the upper air took on increasing importance.

Parachutes and the Weather

Meteorologists in charge of our weather bureaus gradually made discoveries that showed how closely all weather was related. Storms on the surface are only a small part of air movements extending upward to over 30,000 feet. The more they knew about the entire air movement the better they understood the storm.

Up to twenty-five years ago weather observations were limited to those that observers could make from their stations on the ground or, at best, on the top of a high building. Here they could record the air pressure, temperature, humidity, precipitation, and other observable factors. When such data from hundreds of stations were reported by telegraph and plotted on a map, a picture of the air masses on the surface of the earth was obtained. With this weather map and a knowledge of storm movements, it was possible to predict a day or more in advance what the weather would be.

Occasionally a weather observer might go up in an airplane and take observations at 5,000 or perhaps 10,000 feet above ground. Scattered data gathered at these altitudes proved useful to the men of the weather bureaus. It clearly indicated that if more facts about the upper air were known the accuracy of the forecasts would be increased. Airplane weather soundings became a regular part of the weather bureau's work. By 1937, thirty stations were making daily airplane weather observations.

For over forty years the weathermen had been using another device to gather high altitude records. This was nothing more than a balloon to which was attached a box containing automatic recording weather instruments. These would keep a record of changes as the balloon rose through the air. This balloon was turned adrift and carefully observed through a telescope. Observing the balloon not only shows where it is going, but makes it possible to determine the wind directions and speed at different elevations, as the balloon rises.

If the balloon is finally recovered, the record sheet shows the temperature, pressure, and humidity during the balloon's trip. Better balloons and lighter accurate weather instruments were made. Since the record might not be recovered for a week or even a month, if at all, these data could not be used in forecasting. The facts did throw a new light on upper air conditions and paved the way for more advances. These sounding balloons penetrated to heights where the air didn't get much colder as the balloons went higher and higher. This region of uniformly cold air at 70 to 85 degrees below zero is the stratosphere. The stratosphere is a level of constant low temperature, not a fixed height. Naturally it is lower (approximately 4 miles) over the poles than over the tropics (approximately 10 miles). In the stratosphere the air is clear and cold. There are no clouds as there is no water vapor. The winds are constant, undisturbed by storms from below.

Not even stratoliners fly in the stratosphere. All planes travel in the turbulent masses of air nearer the ground. But as the stratosphere is approached the air is calmer, winds are steadier, so there are advantages in upper air travel, at 20,000 to 30,000 feet. It is from this sub-stratosphere region that the free balloons gather weather information.

Sounding balloons go even higher—to heights of 20 miles, far up into the stratosphere. No person has gone this high. From these record heights the balloons have reported new and astounding facts about the air above us.

This method of recording data from the upper air had several limitations. First, it was necessary to recover the balloon in order to obtain the record. Second, if the weather was cloudy or stormy, the balloon could not be followed in its flight. Just at the time they were needed most, observations by pilot balloon and airplane were often impossible. Pilot balloons are still used at over one hundred weather stations. They are economical and furnish information on winds in short order.

For nearly twenty years meteorologists have been seeking a better way to get high altitude data. Their efforts centered in one line of research, the perfection of a radio-meteorograph, an instrument that would transmit weather signals by radio. When carried aloft by a balloon, such a device would send out signals, recording the pressure, temperature, and humidity. These, properly interpreted by a receiver at the weather station, provided the facts.

In 1930 the first successful radio-meteorograph, now more commonly known as radiosonde, was sent aloft near Leningrad, Russia. In 1935 the instrument was first used in this country. A better one was developed for the navy in 1936 and was used in Alaska during the next two years. Radiosonde was continually improved; its weight decreased; its instruments perfected. Recently, in co-operation with the Washington Institute of Technology, a highly improved radiosonde in a plastic case has been designed. These are being made under mass production.

Six airplane weather stations shifted to radiosonde in 1938; others followed, and since 1939 the airplane has been completely displaced by radiosonde in the United States Weather Bureau. The number of radiosonde stations has continually increased. There were thirty in 1939. Now we have about forty in the United States and Alaska. Radiosonde has raised weather forecasting to a new level. Experts have called this instrument the "greatest mechanical improvement in weather forecasting since the invention of the telegraph."

Radiosonde is really a work of art. A tiny box, weighing scarcely two pounds, contains all the equipment to report on the air conditions in altitudes up to ten and twelve miles above the earth. Radiosonde measures the air pressure by means of a tiny barometer. A thermometer records the temperature and a hydrometer indicates the amount of moisture present in the air. As these conditions are measured, an automatic signal is broadcast by means of a tiny short wave radio run on very small batteries. The observer at the radio station picks up these signals or they are received and recorded by an automatic receiver. The balloon is continually recording as it sails through the air. Even in fog, rain, or storm, the radiosonde may be sent aloft.

Perhaps you have been wondering what all this has to do with parachutes. Is such weather knowledge of value to the pilot who may have to jump from a plane at high altitude? Indirectly it is, because the improved weather reports and more accurate predictions make flying at high altitudes safer. It is less likely that unforeseen weather conditions will force the pilot to use his chute.

Actually there is a parachute on the radiosonde itself. Once again the parachute is an economic convenience. The radiosonde is a well-made, valuable instrument. To lose one each time a balloon is sent up would be costly. However, if the radiosonde can be recovered and sent up again and again, the cost of each observation is greatly reduced. The parachute on the radiosonde apparatus makes possible the recovery of the instrument so it may be used again.

When the meteorologist is ready to make a radiosonde observation (since 1941 this is done twice a day at forty stations) he obtains a special latex rubber balloon, a red parachute, and the radiosonde from the supply room. He has available a tank of helium gas. The observer rapidly inflates the balloon with helium until it is about six feet in diameter. He makes no effort to fill the balloon to its maximum content; only getting it large enough to lift the radiosonde and start aloft. If the balloon is sufficiently buoyant, he seals it tight and attaches the apex of the red silk chute to it.

The radiosonde parachute is made of light, thin, red silk and is about a yard and a half square. It is tied with eight shroud lines to a wicker ring about a foot in diameter. This ring prevents the shroud lines from fouling and aids the chute in opening as it falls.

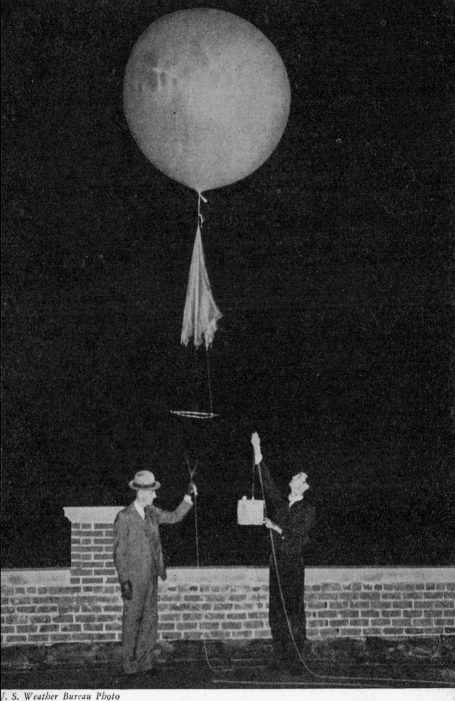

THE SMALL RED PARACHUTE RETURNS THE RADIOSONDE
SAFELY TO EARTH FROM AN EXPLORING TRIP HIGH INTO
THE STRATOSPHERE

Below the ring the lines join together and, at this point, the cord connecting the radiosonde is attached. The instrument is adjusted, the balloon is released, and off it goes.

As the balloon goes higher and higher into the atmosphere, the air pressure becomes less and less. The pressure of the helium gas inside the balloon relatively increases. This increased pressure from within inflates the balloon further. Finally the difference in pressure between the helium inside the balloon and the thin air outside causes the balloon to burst. But by now its work has been done. The radiosonde has ascended higher into the air than planes can fly.

As soon as the balloon bursts the radiosonde starts to fall. The parachute opens and brings the instrument slowly and safely back to earth. The drift of the balloon and of the parachute will land the radiosonde many miles from the weather station.

However, conditions during the ascent of the balloon may interfere. If the balloon rises through moist air, the parachute will become thoroughly soaked and, as it rises higher, the wet chute may freeze. The ice may evaporate at even higher altitudes and the chute becomes free once more. There are a number of conditions that might make it impossible for the chute to open and save the recording instruments. It seems remarkable that any return safely from the trip aloft.

Neatly lettered on the outside of each plastic radiosonde is a message from the weather bureau, telling what the instrument is and asking for its return to the bureau in Washington or to the local weather station. A person returning the radiosonde is not only aiding his country in an important way, but receives a reward of $1.00 as payment for his assistance.

In populated areas the chances are greater for the radiosonde being returned. The percentage of returns varies greatly over the country. On the average, half of the instruments get back to the weather bureau.

Radiosonde may be used in all kinds of weather. Often data from the upper air furnish just the facts needed to make a more accurate forecast. For example, conditions in the upper air may control the time when low clouds or fog will lift. If this time may be estimated accurately it may be possible to schedule a number of plane flights that might have to be canceled otherwise. Radiosonde daily proves its practical worth. Government meteorologists hope for the time when fifty stations or perhaps even more in the United States will be taking daily radiosonde observations to help in weather forecasting. In this task, so essential to air transportation and national welfare, the parachute is doing its small but important part.

Chapter Eighteen

PARACHUTE PROGRESS

COMPARE a modern car with an old 1900 "benzine buggy" and an Airacobra with an old Wright model "B" plane. The progress made in automobiles and airplanes is obvious. But look at an old print of a balloonist parachuting to earth and of a modern paratrooper in the air and you will be more struck by the similarities than the differences. The truth is that the parachute has undergone no fundamental change since the days of Garnerin. It is still the same inverted cup.

The fact that early parachutes worked satisfactorily may be the reason that designs have not been greatly changed. Nobody gets excited about things that work as expected, and parachutes have been doing exactly that for well over two hundred years.

Of course, there has been progress. Every part of the chute has been modified and improved. This progress cannot be overlooked even if it has not revolutionized parachuting. The chute itself, especially the canopy, has been modified a good deal. Modern chutes are smaller than the old balloon chutes. They are stronger and better built. Silk is universally used for the canopy if it is available. If not, modern substitutes are nearly as good.

The vent hole has been altered. Every size from a 6-inch to a 36-inch hole has been tried. Most chutes have a single hole at the apex. The column of air rushing through this hole helps stabilize the chute and limit oscillations. The vent hole is controlled by an elastic ring. As the chute opens and the air in the canopy is put under pressure, the vent opens wider to permit more air to escape. Soon the chute slows down and the pressure is lessened; the rubber ring automatically contracts, reducing the size of the vent hole. The Robar chutes were made with 14 small elastic vents that were designed to act as safety valves under high shock load. Recently an American inventor patented a chute with two vent holes. A cord connects to each hole. By pulling the cord, the chutist can control the size of each vent and, by this means, steer his chute to one side or another.

Another recent parachute is designed with a "dimple" at the apex. The top of the chute is indented like the top of an apple. The cone-shaped opening produced by the "dimple" diverts some of the air from the vent against the inner surface of the canopy. This is supposed to aid the canopy to open faster and to make the chute more steady.

It is not strictly true that canopies are alike. A few types have departed from the full, cup-shaped chute with its scalloped edges. The Russell chute, designed by a parachute engineer who was a member of the original McCook Field group, is made with a distinctly flat top. The edges of the Russell chute are lobed, or turned in, so the widest part of the extended canopy is not at the edge but a short distance above it. The Russell chute has passed all army tests and has been in use for some time. The lobes retard the falling speed and dampen oscillations. The Russell chute does not use a pilot chute to pull it from the pack, yet tests have shown it opens just as fast as those using the pilot chute.

An experimental Russian chute goes to even greater extremes than the Russell design. This chute is practically square, about ten feet to a side. The corners and the edges barely curve over. There are the usual number of shroud lines (24) and a standard harness. No reports are available to show how desirable this adaptation is. Models have been made and have been given field tests. Like practically every other parachute innovation, the shape of this chute is supposed to minimize oscillations.

Still another experimental chute is a triangular one tested by the Army Air Corps at Wright Field, Ohio. This chute was three-cornered with a vent at the center. The shape was designed to give the chute a special advantage. Ordinary chutes may be steered by spilling the air from one side of the canopy by pulling the shroud lines on that side. With a three-cornered chute the air may be spilled from one corner with better control, thus making the chute easier to steer.

In the harness and pack, progress has been made with new materials and designs. It was even suggested that the harness be made of spun glass thread. While there was some doubt as to the ability of the glass to stand the strain, there is no question about a spun glass harness being both fireproof and waterproof. The simplifications in the harness and pack have made this part of the parachute fool-proof. The pack determines the way the parachute will unfold. It controls the possibility of lines fouling, as they are pulled from their pockets. When chutes are packed according to the manufacturer's detailed instructions, there is practically no chance of anything going wrong as the chute opens.

Several types of packs have been perfected for convenience of airmen using different planes and doing special work on board. Just before World War II started, the chute companies were working on packs that fitted the seats of private and transport planes. These packs were practically invisible, but passengers could adjust the straps in a few seconds and be ready to jump in an emergency.

THIS SQUARE EXPERIMENTAL CHUTE ILLUSTRATES ONE
LINE OF PARACHUTE PROGRESS. TRIANGULAR CHUTES
HAVE ALSO BEEN TRIED

Parachutes

New uses for parachutes are continually reported. One striking example comes from the Post Office Department. Rapid mail delivery has been impossible in the rugged Appalachian region extending from Kentucky to West Virginia, Pennsylvania, and New York. Air mail did not help much as there was not enough mail to start full service and, besides, flying conditions over the mountains are notoriously bad.

The problem was solved by some young men who organized the All American Aviation Company. Now air mail is picked up and delivered to over a hundred Appalachian stations. The service is growing and the idea is applicable to many other thinly populated areas. In this system two 20-foot "goal-posts" are erected, 20 feet apart on the airfield. These posts are made of light metal and bamboo. Suspended between them is a transfer rope to which the mail container is attached. This container is 8 by 8 by 17 inches and holds up to 50 pounds of mail. The entire apparatus can be set up in three minutes. The mail plane swoops low over the posts at about 100 miles an hour. The pouch to be delivered is released and falls to the ground. Almost at the same moment, the pick-up boom, extending below the plane, catches the transfer rope attached to the pouch of outgoing mail. A powerful shock absorber prevents the rope from breaking, and a winch pulls the pouch into the plane.

The delivery of fragile articles or articles that are too large to fit into the special container is made by parachute. Each pick-up plane is equipped with several small chutes, approximately 12 feet in diameter. These are released just before the pick-up is made and usually reach the ground in the vicinity of the "goalposts." Since they are dropped from a low altitude the chutes cannot drift far and be lost.

The Air Mail Pick-up Service has completed a million miles of flying in a year and a quarter. It has made over 50,000 pick-ups and deliveries, totaling a quarter of a million pounds of mail. The service includes five routes that cover 112 cities. It has undergone severe practical tests and has reached a stage comparable to the regular air mail service. Despite the difficulties of mountain flying, 95% of the scheduled flights have been completed. Rural communities are brought closer to the cities this way. Not only mail but urgently needed serums, vaccines, and medical supplies can be delivered to doctors and isolated hospitals. This is still another job for parachutes.

The problem of rescuing passengers of disabled transport planes has received a good deal of attention. Parachute designers point out the strict rules that require everyone in a military plane to wear a chute. They call attention to the many lives saved because of this precaution; not only lives of pilots but of untrained soldiers being transported from one base to another. When one army bomber ran into engine trouble over the Rocky Mountains, seven privates on board and the crew parachuted to safety. If they had stayed with the ship they would have had little chance to survive.

The other side of the story is concerned with increased air safety, the lack of time to jump in an emergency, and the possibility of panic. There is probably much to be said on both sides and the problems involved must be carefully considered. Many an official wishes the rescue problem from transport planes could be settled in the simple way one naive inventor did, not long ago. This man obtained a patent on an improved rescue device for commercial planes. Each seat in the plane was equipped with a chute pack. In an emergency the passengers buckle the straps around them. The pilot pulls a lever, the floor of the plane tilts down, each seat falls backward and the passengers tumble merrily head over heels through the gaping hole at the rear of the plane. If they are not too surprised to pull the rip cord, all will go well.

There have been more serious suggestions and improvements. The Russian automatic chute has possibilities. This chute opens by itself at a set time after the passenger jumps. No rip cord is used. The harness in some models is now controlled by a single catch. This can be quickly fastened, and released just as fast when the chute hits ground.

Another line of progress with parachutes follows an entirely different slant. The work is still in its experimental stages, but there are many who feel that there will be a place for plane chutes. The idea is simple. Instead of the pilot leaping to safety with a parachute, why not drop the whole plane slowly and easily to the ground?

The first experiments with plane-landing chutes

were made nearly fifteen years ago in California. A number of techniques were tried. In one attempt, the pilot took up a 2,600-pound plane. When he gained safe altitude he cut the ignition, released a 60-foot parachute that had been attached to the fuselage, and then jumped himself. The pilot pulled his rip cord and floated down. The plane also came down easily. The big chute opened, checked the plane in mid-air, and slowly settled it groundward. The plane hit on a hard three-point landing that crumpled the under-carriage, but beside this minor damage it was unin-jured.

With other planes 50-foot and 65-foot chutes were used. They all seemed satisfactory. Planes dropped at an average speed of 15 feet per second, slow enough to reduce damage greatly. A 65-foot Russell chute tested on the ground and in the air satisfied the en-gineers conducting the experiment.

Other large plane-carrying chutes have been built. The largest has a diameter of 100 feet. The huge canopy has seven vent holes but otherwise it is similar to other chutes. In tests this chute has lowered weights of over 10,000 pounds. An 84-foot chute designed by

Major Hoffman has also worked well. It easily lowered a 1,600-pound plane. This chute has been tested recently at Wright Field in Ohio.

About the same time experiments were conducted in which the parachute was used as an air brake. Often emergency landings are impossible because a long field or runway is needed. If the speed of the plane could be checked immediately after it hit the ground, such emergency landings would be safer. On aircraft carriers special devices slow down the plane as soon as it hits deck, but these are unsuited for ground use. Why not try a parachute? In this experiment the small plane went up as usual and landed as usual, but as soon as the wheels hit the ground the pilot released the large chute from its tail. The forward speed of the plane and the slipstream wind opened the chute immediately. The breaking effect of the canopy was terrific and it pulled the plane to a dead stop in its tracks. The landing distance was reduced to a small fraction of the space usually needed.

There is one last form of a plane chute, which, if it is ever used, will never save a life. This is because it is designed to work on a radio-controlled plane that soars aloft without a pilot. It is guided from the ground by radio impulses. This idea is not new, but no radio-controlled plane has ever been equipped with a parachute before. The parachute is ready to work when the radio fails. A radio plane that does not receive control signals is worse than useless—it is a danger to people below.

In this new model, a large plane chute is packed in the cabin or in a container and is held in place by an electromagnetic lock. The same carrier wave that controls the plane keeps the parachute locked in place. If the plane should get out of range or if anything should go wrong with the radio, the impulse holding the lock shut would no longer operate. The door swings open and the parachute streams out. As the door opens, the ignition is automatically cut off and from then on the parachute takes over.

These are the lines of parachute progress. Small modifications, new designs, new uses; each making the parachute a little better and of greater service. Since so many parachutes are being used in this war, under so many different conditions, it is probable that new ideas for parachute design and use will emerge. These will, in turn, lead to further changes. Whether all of these changes will be of practical value only time will tell.

INDEX

(Asterisk after a number signifies illustration)

249

Index

Index

Index